Problem Solvers

Edited by L. Marder
Senior Lecturer in Mathematics, University of Southampton

No. 3

Vector Algebra

Problem Solvers

Vector Algebra

L. MARDER

Senior Lecturer in Mathematics
University of Southampton

London
GEORGE ALLEN & UNWIN
Boston   Sydney

First published in 1971
Second impression 1978

GEORGE ALLEN & UNWIN LTD
40 Museum Street, London WC1A 1LU

© George Allen & Unwin (Publishers) Ltd, 1971

ISBN 0 04 512012 9 *paper*

ISBN 0 04 512013 7 *cased*

Printed in Great Britain in 10 on 12pt Times
by Biddles Ltd, Guildford, Surrey

Contents

Chapter 1

Basic Operations

1.1 Definitions   A *scalar* is any quantity with magnitude but no direction; e.g. temperature, mass. electric charge, work. It is specified by a real number when appropriate units have been chosen. A *vector* is a quantity with both magnitude and direction, e.g. force, displacement, velocity, acceleration. It is specified by a positive real number (called the *magnitude*) and a direction, when units have been chosen. A vector can always be represented as a displacement from any initial point O in space to a terminal point P, such that the direction of the line-segment OP is the direction of the vector, while the distance OP (in a suitable scale) is its magnitude. If O' and P' are a second pair of points for which the line-segment $O'P'$ has the same direction and length as OP, then the two displacements represent the same vector.

A vector is usually denoted by a single bold letter thus: **a**, with magnitude denoted by $|\mathbf{a}|$ or a. Two vectors **a** and **b** are *equal* if they have the same magnitude and direction, and we write $\mathbf{a} = \mathbf{b}$. We might also write $\mathbf{OP} = \mathbf{O'P'}$ in the above example to denote equality of the two *displacement vectors*. The *zero vector* is any vector of zero magnitude, and is denoted by the symbol **0**. The *negative* of a vector **a** is the vector with the same magnitude but opposite direction to that of **a**. It is written $-\mathbf{a}$.

The *sum* or *resultant* of **a** and **b** is defined according to the 'triangle law of addition' as follows. Let **a** be drawn with initial point O and terminal point P, and let **b** be drawn with initial point P and terminal point Q. Then the sum of **a** and **b** is the vector $\mathbf{a} + \mathbf{b} = \mathbf{b} + \mathbf{a} = \mathbf{OQ}$. If we add a third vector **c** to this sum, we easily find that $(\mathbf{a}+\mathbf{b})+\mathbf{c} = \mathbf{a}+(\mathbf{b}+\mathbf{c})$, so that brackets are unnecessary, and the sum may be denoted by $\mathbf{a}+\mathbf{b}+\mathbf{c}$. The order in which the three vectors appear in this sum is immaterial.

The *difference* between **a** and **b** (or the vector obtained by *subtracting* **b** from **a**) is defined to be $\mathbf{a}+(-\mathbf{b})$, written $\mathbf{a}-\mathbf{b}$.

Problem 1.1   A ship sails 50 km due north and then 95 km southwest. Find the resultant displacement.

Solution. In Fig. 1.1, $\mathbf{a} = \mathbf{PQ}$ represents the displacement 50 km due north and $\mathbf{b} = \mathbf{QR}$ represents, to the same scale, the displacement 95 km southwest. The resultant displacement is represented by $\mathbf{c} = \mathbf{a}+\mathbf{b} = \mathbf{PR}$. By the cosine formula,

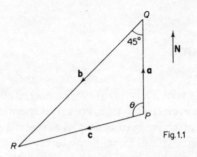

Fig. 1.1

$$c^2 = a^2 + b^2 - 2ab\cos 45° = 2500 + 9025 - 2(50)(95)(1/\sqrt{2})$$
$$= 11\,525 - 6717 = 4808,$$

giving $c = 69\cdot3$ (km), approximately.

By the sine formula

$$\frac{c}{\sin 45°} = \frac{b}{\sin QPR},$$

whence, if $\theta = QPR$,

$$\sin\theta = \frac{95}{69\cdot3}\sin 45° = 0\cdot968,$$

or $\theta = 105°30'$. Thus, the resultant displacement is $69\cdot3$ km in the direction $14°30'$ south of west. This result could also be found graphically from an accurate scale diagram by measurement of PR and θ. ☐

Problem 1.2 If $\mathbf{a}, \mathbf{b}, \mathbf{c}, \mathbf{d}$ denote the displacements from A to B, B to C, C to D, and D to A, respectively, where $ABCD$ is a square, indicate on a diagram the vectors $\mathbf{a} + \mathbf{b}$, $-\mathbf{b}$, $\mathbf{a} - \mathbf{b}$, and evaluate the sum $\mathbf{a} + \mathbf{b} + \mathbf{c} + \mathbf{d}$.

Solution. In Fig. 1.2, E is on CB produced, and $EB = BC$. We have

$$\mathbf{AC} = \mathbf{AB} + \mathbf{BC} = \mathbf{a} + \mathbf{b},$$
$$\mathbf{BE} = -\mathbf{BC} = -\mathbf{b},$$
$$\mathbf{AE} = \mathbf{AB} + \mathbf{BE} = \mathbf{a} + (-\mathbf{b}) = \mathbf{a} - \mathbf{b}.$$

The sum of the vectors $\mathbf{a}, \mathbf{b}, \mathbf{c}, \mathbf{d}$ corresponds to the resultant of the displacements $\mathbf{AB}, \mathbf{BC}, \mathbf{CD}, \mathbf{DA}$, i.e. to the zero displacement from A to A. Hence $\mathbf{a} + \mathbf{b} + \mathbf{c} + \mathbf{d} = 0$. ☐

1.2 Multiplication of a Vector by a Scalar Let $\mathbf{a}$ be any vector and c any positive real number. The vector $c\mathbf{a}$ is defined to be that vector in the direction of $\mathbf{a}$ with magnitude $c|\mathbf{a}|$. If d is any negative real number, then $d\mathbf{a}$ is defined to be the vector $-|d|\mathbf{a}$, where $|d|$ denotes the absolute value of d. It is in the opposite direction to that of $\mathbf{a}$. Since any scalar can be regarded

2

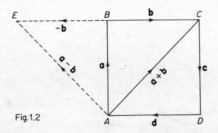

Fig.1.2

as a real number, the multiplication of a vector by a scalar is likewise defined.

A *unit* vector is one of unit magnitude. The unit vector in the direction of any given non-zero vector **a** is denoted by **â**. Thus,

$$\hat{\mathbf{a}} = \frac{1}{a}\mathbf{a} \quad \text{or} \quad \mathbf{a} = a\hat{\mathbf{a}}.$$

Problem 1.3 Let **a** and **b** be non-parallel vectors. Indicate on a diagram the vector $\frac{3}{2}\mathbf{b} - \frac{1}{2}\mathbf{a}$.

Solution. In Fig. 1.3, **PQ** represents **a** and **RS** represents **b**. From any point A is drawn AB parallel to RS, such that $AB = \frac{3}{2}RS$. From B is drawn BC parallel to QP, such that $BC = \frac{1}{2}QP$. Then

$$\mathbf{AB} = \tfrac{3}{2}\mathbf{b}, \quad \mathbf{BC} = -\tfrac{1}{2}\mathbf{a}, \quad \mathbf{AC} = \mathbf{AB} + \mathbf{BC} = \tfrac{3}{2}\mathbf{b} - \tfrac{1}{2}\mathbf{a}. \qquad \square$$

Fig. 1.3

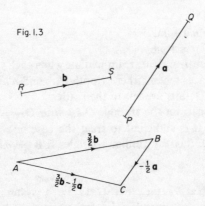

Problem 1.4 Let **a** and **b** be the *position vectors* of the points P and Q, respectively, relative to the origin O. Prove that the point R which divides PQ in the ratio $m:n$ (n positive) has position vector **c** relative to O, where

$$\mathbf{c} = \frac{n\mathbf{a} + m\mathbf{b}}{m+n}.$$

3

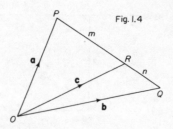

Fig. I.4

Solution. The *position vector* of a point, P say, relative to a second point O, is the vector $\mathbf{OP}$. In the case depicted in Fig. 1.4, R is an internal point of PQ. We have

$$PR = \frac{m}{n}RQ = \frac{m}{m+n}PQ, \tag{1.1}$$

and therefore

$$\mathbf{c} = \mathbf{OR} = \mathbf{OP} + \mathbf{PR}$$

$$= \mathbf{a} + \frac{m}{m+n}(\mathbf{b} - \mathbf{a}) = \frac{n\mathbf{a} + m\mathbf{b}}{m+n}. \tag{1.2}$$

Equation (1.1) remains valid when R is an external point of PQ, as is easily seen from a diagram, and (1.2) is true in all cases. ☐

Problem 1.5 Prove that for any real numbers m and n, and vectors $\mathbf{a}$ and $\mathbf{b}$:

(i) $(mn)\mathbf{a} = m(n\mathbf{a})$,

(ii) $(m+n)\mathbf{a} = m\mathbf{a} + n\mathbf{a}$,

(iii) $m(\mathbf{a} + \mathbf{b}) = m\mathbf{a} + m\mathbf{b}$.

Solution. Formulae (i) and (ii) are immediate when each side is represented on a diagram, the cases when either or both of m and n are negative being treated separately. Details are left to the reader.

To prove (iii), construct the triangle OAB with $\mathbf{OA} = \mathbf{a}$, $\mathbf{AB} = \mathbf{b}$, and hence $\mathbf{OB} = \mathbf{a} + \mathbf{b}$. It is sufficient to treat the case $m > 0$. If $\mathbf{OA'} = m\mathbf{a}$ and $\mathbf{OB'} = m(\mathbf{a} + \mathbf{b})$, then by similar triangles $\mathbf{A'B'} = m\mathbf{b}$, and the result follows. ☐

1.3 Components of a Vector Let $Oxyz$ be a system of rectangular cartesian coordinate axes, as in Fig. 1.5. Imagine a right-handed corkscrew to lie along Oz with its handle in the xy plane. If the rotation of the handle in the sense which takes Ox into Oy (through 90°) would cause the screw to move in the direction Oz, then the system is said to be *right-handed*. Thus, in Fig. 1.5, Ox would be directed out of the plane of the diagram. If the direction of one of the axes, say Ox, of a right-handed system is

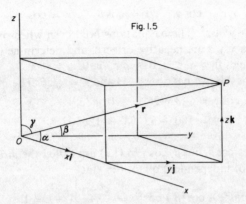

Fig. 1.5

reversed, the system becomes *left-handed*. By convention, unless stated otherwise, we shall always assume that a system is right-handed.

The set of mutually orthogonal unit vectors, denoted by **i**, **j**, **k**, having the directions Ox, Oy, and Oz, respectively, is important. If **r** is any vector represented with initial point O and terminal point P, the coordinates of P being (x, y, z), then we may write $\mathbf{r} = x\mathbf{i} + y\mathbf{j} + z\mathbf{k}$. Any vector **r** may be represented as a sum of three vectors in the directions **i**, **j**, **k** in this way, the numbers x, y, and z being uniquely determined by **r**. We call (x, y, z) the *rectangular components* of **r** in the directions **i**, **j**, and **k**; the individual components may be positive, negative or zero. Clearly, the magnitude of **r** is $r = \sqrt{(x^2 + y^2 + z^2)}$.

The addition or subtraction of vectors expressed in component form is carried out by simply adding or subtracting corresponding components.

Problem 1.6 If A is the point $(3, 1, 2)$ and B the point $(-1, 2, -1)$, express the vector **AB** in component form and evaluate $|\mathbf{AB}|$.

Solution. We have

$$\mathbf{OA} = 3\mathbf{i} + \mathbf{j} + 2\mathbf{k}, \quad \mathbf{OB} = -\mathbf{i} + 2\mathbf{j} - \mathbf{k},$$

and therefore

$$\mathbf{AB} = \mathbf{OB} - \mathbf{OA} = \mathbf{i} + 2\mathbf{j} - \mathbf{k} - (3\mathbf{i} + \mathbf{j} + 2\mathbf{k})$$
$$= -4\mathbf{i} + \mathbf{j} - 3\mathbf{k},$$

and $\quad |\mathbf{AB}| = \text{dist. } AB = \sqrt{[(-4)^2 + 1^2 + (-3)^2]} = \sqrt{26}.$ ☐

Problem 1.7 If $\mathbf{r} = x\mathbf{i} + y\mathbf{j} + z\mathbf{k}$, find the angles α, β, and γ between **r** and the directions of Ox, Oy, and Oz, respectively. What is the angle between **AB** and Oz in Problem 1.6?

Solution. Construct the rectangular solid (Fig. 1.5) with $x\mathbf{i}$, $y\mathbf{j}$, and $z\mathbf{k}$ as edges, O being one vertex. We have,

5

$$x/r = \cos\alpha, \quad y/r = \cos\beta, \quad z/r = \cos\gamma, \tag{1.3}$$

where $r^2 = x^2 + y^2 + z^2$. These equations hold even when one or more of the components x, y, z are negative or zero, and determine unique angles α, β, γ in the ranges $0 \leqslant \alpha \leqslant \pi, 0 \leqslant \beta \leqslant \pi, 0 \leqslant \gamma \leqslant \pi$.

For the vector **AB**, we have $z = -3$ and $r = \sqrt{26}$. Therefore,

$$\cos\gamma = -3/\sqrt{26} = -0 \cdot 5883,$$

whence
$$\gamma = 180° - 53° \, 58' = 126° \, 02'. \qquad \blacksquare$$

The quantities $\cos\alpha, \cos\beta, \cos\gamma$ in (1.3) are called the *direction cosines* of **r**. They are not independent quantities since

$$\cos^2\alpha + \cos^2\beta + \cos^2\gamma = \frac{x^2 + y^2 + z^2}{r^2} = 1.$$

Problem 1.8 Forces $\mathbf{F}_1 = 2\mathbf{i} + 3\mathbf{j} - \mathbf{k}$, $\mathbf{F}_2 = -5\mathbf{i} + \mathbf{j} + 2\mathbf{k}$, $\mathbf{F}_3 = 6\mathbf{i} - \mathbf{k}$ (newtons) act simultaneously on a particle. Find the magnitude and direction of the resultant force.

Solution. The resultant force **F** is the vector sum of the individual forces. Thus

$$\begin{aligned} \mathbf{F} = \mathbf{F}_1 + \mathbf{F}_2 + \mathbf{F}_3 &= 2\mathbf{i} + 3\mathbf{j} - \mathbf{k} + (-5\mathbf{i} + \mathbf{j} + 2\mathbf{k}) + (6\mathbf{i} - \mathbf{k}) \\ &= 3\mathbf{i} + 4\mathbf{j}. \end{aligned}$$

Its magnitude is $\sqrt{(3^2 + 4^2)} = 5$ (newtons).

Since the z component of **F** is zero, the resultant force is parallel to the xy plane. The direction is in the first quadrant, making an angle α with Ox, where $\cos\alpha = \frac{3}{5}$, so that $\alpha = 53° \, 08'$.

The resultant force can also be written in the form $\mathbf{F} = F\hat{\mathbf{a}}$, where $F = 5$ is the magnitude and $\hat{\mathbf{a}} = \frac{1}{5}(3\mathbf{i} + 4\mathbf{j})$ is a unit vector specifying the direction. $\qquad \blacksquare$

1.4 Linear Dependence and Independence If three vectors **a**, **b**, **c** are not all parallel to any one plane, they are said to be *non-coplanar*. (Otherwise, they are *coplanar*.) Given any vector **r**, we may construct a parallelepiped with diagonal OP, where $\mathbf{r} = \mathbf{OP}$, and whose edges are respectively parallel to **a**, **b**, **c**. Thus, a vector can always be expressed (uniquely) as the sum of three vectors in given non-coplanar directions, i.e. we can choose numbers l, m, n such that

$$\mathbf{r} = l\mathbf{a} + m\mathbf{b} + n\mathbf{c}. \tag{1.4}$$

Problem 1.9 Let $\mathbf{a} = 2\mathbf{i} + \mathbf{j}$, $\mathbf{b} = 3\mathbf{i} - \mathbf{j} + \mathbf{k}$, $\mathbf{c} = -\mathbf{i} + 2\mathbf{j} + 2\mathbf{k}$, and $\mathbf{r} = -8\mathbf{i} + \mathbf{j} + \mathbf{k}$. Determine l, m, n in (1.4).

Solution. We have to satisfy the relations

$$-8\mathbf{i}+\mathbf{j}+\mathbf{k} = l(2\mathbf{i}+\mathbf{j})+m(3\mathbf{i}-\mathbf{j}+\mathbf{k})+n(-\mathbf{i}+2\mathbf{j}+2\mathbf{k})$$
$$= (2l+3m-n)\mathbf{i}+(l-m+2n)\mathbf{j}+(m+2n)\mathbf{k}.$$

Since any vector has unique components relative to the base vectors $\mathbf{i}, \mathbf{j}, \mathbf{k}$, we can equate corresponding components on the two sides, obtaining the simultaneous equations:

$$2l+3m-n = -8, \quad l-m+2n = 1, \quad m+2n = 1. \tag{1.5}$$

Solving, we get $l = -2$, $m = -1$, $n = 1$, and $\mathbf{r} = -2\mathbf{a}-\mathbf{b}+\mathbf{c}$. $\quad\square$

Problem 1.10 Why does the construction in the last problem fail if $\mathbf{c}$ is replaced by $\mathbf{c} = -5\mathbf{i}+5\mathbf{j}-3\mathbf{k}$?

Solution. Corresponding to (1.5) we now find

$$2l+3m-5n = -8, \quad l-m+5n = 1, \quad m-3n = 1.$$

Eliminating l from the first two equations gives $m-3n = -2$, which is incompatible with the last equation. In this case the vectors $\mathbf{a}$, $\mathbf{b}$ and $\mathbf{c}$ are coplanar since $\mathbf{c} = 2\mathbf{a}-3\mathbf{b}$, which shows that $\mathbf{c}$ is in the plane of $\mathbf{a}$ and $\mathbf{b}$. Unless the vector $\mathbf{r}$ is in this plane too, it cannot be expressed in the form (1.4). If $\mathbf{r}$ is parallel to the same plane as the coplanar vectors $\mathbf{a}, \mathbf{b}, \mathbf{c}$, it can be expressed in the form (1.4), but the coefficients l, m, n are not uniquely determined. $\quad\square$

Problem 1.11 Prove that any 4 vectors are *linearly dependent*.

Solution. A set of n vectors $\mathbf{r}_1, \mathbf{r}_2, \ldots, \mathbf{r}_n$ is said to be *linearly dependent* if there are real numbers $c_1, c_2, \ldots, c_n$, not all zero, such that

$$c_1\mathbf{r}_1 +c_2\mathbf{r}_2 +\ldots+c_n\mathbf{r}_n = 0. \tag{1.6}$$

Let $n = 4$. Suppose first that none of the given vectors is the zero vector. If $\mathbf{r}_1, \mathbf{r}_2, \mathbf{r}_3$ are non-coplanar, then we can express $\mathbf{r}_4$ in the form

$$\mathbf{r}_4 = l\mathbf{r}_1 +m\mathbf{r}_2 +n\mathbf{r}_3,$$

according to (1.4), where l, m, n are not all zero since $\mathbf{r}_4$ is not the zero vector. This relation can be written $l\mathbf{r}_1+m\mathbf{r}_2+n\mathbf{r}_3+(-1)\mathbf{r}_4 = 0$, which is in the form (1.6).

If $\mathbf{r}_1, \mathbf{r}_2, \mathbf{r}_3$ are coplanar, then if $\mathbf{r}_1, \mathbf{r}_2$ are not collinear (i.e. not in the same or opposite directions) then we can evidently write $\mathbf{r}_3 = p\mathbf{r}_1+q\mathbf{r}_2$, for some real numbers p and q, not both zero. Thus,

$$p\mathbf{r}_1+q\mathbf{r}_2-\mathbf{r}_3 = 0,$$

which is of the form (1.6) with $c_4 = 0$. Finally, if $\mathbf{r}_1, \mathbf{r}_2$ are collinear there is a relation $\mathbf{r}_1 = k\mathbf{r}_2$ for some real number k, which we can write as $\mathbf{r}_1-k\mathbf{r}_2 = 0$, which is again of the required form, with $c_3 = c_4 = 0$.

When one of the given vectors, r_1 say, is the zero vector, then (1.6) holds with $c_1 = 1$ and all other c's equal to zero.

Note: An immediate extension of this argument shows that more than four vectors are always linearly dependent. When vectors are not linearly dependent they are *linearly independent*. □

Problem 1.12 Give a determinantal condition for the vectors

$$r_1 = \alpha_1 i + \beta_1 j + \gamma_1 k, \quad r_2 = \alpha_2 i + \beta_2 j + \gamma_2 k, \quad r_3 = \alpha_3 i + \beta_3 j + \gamma_3 k$$

to be linearly dependent.

Solution. The vectors are linearly dependent if and only if there are real numbers c_1, c_2, c_3, not all zero, such that $c_1 r_1 + c_2 r_2 + c_3 r_3 = 0$. On equating to zero the coefficients of i, j, k in turn we get

$$c_1 \alpha_1 + c_2 \alpha_2 + c_3 \alpha_3 = 0, \quad c_1 \beta_1 + c_2 \beta_2 + c_3 \beta_3 = 0, \quad c_1 \gamma_1 + c_2 \gamma_2 + c_3 \gamma_3 = 0.$$

These linear equations are compatible, under the condition that the c's are not all zero, if and only if the determinant

$$\begin{vmatrix} \alpha_1 & \alpha_2 & \alpha_3 \\ \beta_1 & \beta_2 & \beta_3 \\ \gamma_1 & \gamma_2 & \gamma_3 \end{vmatrix} = 0. \tag{1.7}$$

□

Problem 1.13 Test for coplanarity the vectors a, b, c in Problem 1.10.

Solution. In this case the determinant (1.7) is

$$\begin{vmatrix} 2 & 1 & 0 \\ 3 & -1 & 1 \\ -5 & 5 & -3 \end{vmatrix} = 2 \begin{vmatrix} -1 & 1 \\ 5 & -3 \end{vmatrix} - \begin{vmatrix} 3 & 1 \\ -5 & -3 \end{vmatrix} = 0.$$

Hence the vectors a, b, c are coplanar. □

Problem 1.14 Let $P_1, P_2, \ldots, P_n$ be points with position vectors $a_1, a_2, \ldots, a_n$ relative to the origin. Prove that if $c_1, c_2, \ldots, c_n$ are real numbers such that

$$c_1 a_1 + c_2 a_2 + \ldots + c_n a_n = 0, \tag{1.8}$$

then this relation is independent of the choice of origin if, and only if,

$$\sum_{i=1}^{n} c_i = 0.$$

Solution. Suppose that (1.8) is valid for given values of the c's when the origin is the point O. Let any other point O' be chosen as new origin. If $b = OO'$, then the position vector of the point P_i relative to O' is $a_i' = a_i - b$ $(i = 1, 2, \ldots, n)$. Then

8

$$c_1\mathbf{a}_1' + c_2\mathbf{a}_2' + \ldots + c_n\mathbf{a}_n' = c_1(\mathbf{a}_1 - \mathbf{b}) + c_2(\mathbf{a}_2 - \mathbf{b}) + \ldots + c_n(\mathbf{a}_n - \mathbf{b})$$
$$= -(c_1 + c_2 + \ldots + c_n)\mathbf{b}, \qquad \text{by (1.8)},$$
$$= 0,$$

for all $\mathbf{b}$ if, and only if, $\sum\limits_{i=1}^{n} c_i = 0$. $\qquad\square$

The *centroid* or *mass centre* of masses $m_1, m_2, \ldots, m_n$ located at points whose position vectors relative to the origin O are $\mathbf{r}_1, \mathbf{r}_2, \ldots, \mathbf{r}_n$, respectively, is defined to be the point G with position vector $\mathbf{r}$ relative to O, where

$$\mathbf{r} = \frac{m_1\mathbf{r}_1 + m_2\mathbf{r}_2 + \ldots + m_n\mathbf{r}_n}{m_1 + m_2 + \ldots + m_n}. \qquad (1.9)$$

Problem 1.15 Find the centroid of masses 5, 3 and 2 units, respectively, at the vertices $A = (1, 0, 2)$, $B = (2, -3, 1)$ and $C = (4, 7, 2)$ of the triangle ABC.

Solution. By definition, the position vector $\mathbf{r}$ of the centroid G is given by

$$(5 + 3 + 2)\mathbf{r} = 5(\mathbf{i} + 2\mathbf{k}) + 3(2\mathbf{i} - 3\mathbf{j} + \mathbf{k}) + 2(4\mathbf{i} + 7\mathbf{j} + 2\mathbf{k}),$$

whence $\qquad\qquad \mathbf{r} = \tfrac{1}{10}(19\mathbf{i} + 5\mathbf{j} + 17\mathbf{k}).$ $\qquad\square$

Problem 1.16 Prove that the centroid (1.9) is independent of the origin.

Solution. Write (1.9) as

$$(\textstyle\sum m_i)\mathbf{r} - \sum m_i\mathbf{r}_i = 0.$$

This linear relation between the $n + 1$ vectors $\mathbf{r}, \mathbf{r}_1, \mathbf{r}_2, \ldots, \mathbf{r}_n$ is independent of the origin because the sum of the coefficients is

$$(\textstyle\sum m_i) - \sum m_i = 0.$$

(Here we have used the result in Problem 1.14.) $\qquad\square$

Problem 1.17 Prove that the centroid of masses m_1, m_2, m_3, situated at the vertices A, B, C of a triangle, lies in the plane of the triangle.

Solution. Consider (1.9), where we put $n = 3$. If the centroid itself is chosen as origin O, and if $\mathbf{r}_1, \mathbf{r}_2, \mathbf{r}_3$ are the position vectors of A, B, C, respectively, relative to this origin, then $OG = 0$, so that

$$0 = \frac{m_1\mathbf{r}_1 + m_2\mathbf{r}_2 + m_3\mathbf{r}_3}{m_1 + m_2 + m_3}.$$

Thus, $\qquad\qquad \mathbf{r}_3 = a\mathbf{r}_1 + b\mathbf{r}_2,$

where $a = -m_1/m_3$, $b = -m_2/m_3$. That is,

$$\mathbf{OC} = a\mathbf{OA} + b\mathbf{OB},$$

which shows that **OC** is in the plane determined by **OA** and **OB**. It follows that the centroid G is in the plane of A, B and C. ◻

1.5 The Scalar Product The *scalar product* or *dot product* of two vectors **a** and **b** is the real number $ab \cos \theta$, where θ $(0 \leqslant \theta \leqslant \pi)$ is the angle between the directions of **a** and **b**. When the vectors **a** and **b** are perpendicular, the scalar product vanishes. When **a** and **b** have the same direction the scalar product is equal to ab.

This important product, denoted by **a . b**, has the following evident properties (m being any real number):

(i) $\mathbf{a . b} = \mathbf{b . a}$,   (ii) $\mathbf{a . a} = a^2$,   (iii) $(m\mathbf{a}).\mathbf{b} = m(\mathbf{a.b}) = \mathbf{a}.(m\mathbf{b})$.   (1.10)

Problem 1.18   Prove the *distributive law*

$$\mathbf{a}.(\mathbf{b}+\mathbf{c}) = \mathbf{a}.\mathbf{b}+\mathbf{a}.\mathbf{c}. \tag{1.11}$$

Solution. Draw **a** and **b** with common initial point P and with terminal points Q and R respectively. Draw **c** with initial point R and terminal point S. By definition, **a . b** is equal to

$$PQ . PR \cos RPQ = PQ . PR',$$

where PR' is the projection of PR on the line PQ. Likewise, **a . c** is equal to $PQ . R'S'$, where $R'S'$ is the projection of RS on the line PQ. Adding the two results gives

$$\mathbf{a.b}+\mathbf{a.c} = PQ(PR'+R'S') = PQ . PS' = \mathbf{a}.(\mathbf{b}+\mathbf{c}),$$

since PS' is the projection of PS on PQ.

Note: Another form of distributive law, easily obtained from (1.11) and (1.10i) is

$$(\mathbf{b}+\mathbf{c}).\mathbf{a} = \mathbf{b.a}+\mathbf{c.a}. \qquad\qquad ◻ \quad (1.12)$$

Problem 1.19   Use the scalar product to find the angle between the vectors $\mathbf{a} = 6\mathbf{i}-3\mathbf{j}+\mathbf{k}$, $\mathbf{b} = 2\mathbf{i}+2\mathbf{j}-\mathbf{k}$.

Solution. Let the required angle be $\theta (0 \leqslant \theta \leqslant \pi)$. We have

$$\mathbf{a.b} = ab \cos \theta = (6\mathbf{i}-3\mathbf{j}+\mathbf{k}).(2\mathbf{i}+2\mathbf{j}-\mathbf{k}).$$

Now, $\mathbf{i.i} = \mathbf{j.j} = \mathbf{k.k} = 1$, $\mathbf{i.j} = \mathbf{j.i} = \mathbf{j.k} = \mathbf{k.j} = \mathbf{k.i} = \mathbf{i.k} = 0$.

Hence, using (1.11) and (1.12),

$$\mathbf{a.b} = (6)(2)+(-3)(2)+(1)(-1) = 12-6-1 = 5.$$

But $a^2 = \mathbf{a.a} = (6)(6)+(-3)(-3)+(1)(1) = 46,$

$$b^2 = \mathbf{b.b} = (2)(2)+(2)(2)+(-1)(-1) = 9,$$

and so $$\cos \theta = \frac{\mathbf{a.b}}{ab} = \frac{5}{3\sqrt{46}},$$

$$\theta = 75° \, 46'.$$

10

We note from this problem that if $\mathbf{a} = a_1\mathbf{i} + a_2\mathbf{j} + a_3\mathbf{k}, \mathbf{b} = b_1\mathbf{i} + b_2\mathbf{j} + b_3\mathbf{k}$, then

$$\mathbf{a}.\mathbf{a} = a_1^2 + a_2^2 + a_3^2, \qquad \mathbf{a}.\mathbf{b} = a_1 b_1 + a_2 b_2 + a_3 b_3. \qquad \square \quad (1.13)$$

Problem 1.20 Find a unit vector orthogonal to both the vectors $\mathbf{a} = 8\mathbf{i} + 2\mathbf{j} - \mathbf{k}, \mathbf{b} = 3\mathbf{i} - \mathbf{j} - 3\mathbf{k}$.

Solution. Let $\mathbf{c} = c_1\mathbf{i} + c_2\mathbf{j} + c_3\mathbf{k}$ be any vector orthogonal to both $\mathbf{a}$ and $\mathbf{b}$. Then $\mathbf{a}.\mathbf{c} = \mathbf{b}.\mathbf{c} = 0$, giving

$$8c_1 + 2c_2 - c_3 = 0, \qquad 3c_1 - c_2 - 3c_3 = 0.$$

Solving, we get $c_3 = 2c_1, c_2 = -3c_1$. Therefore

$$\mathbf{c} = c_1(\mathbf{i} - 3\mathbf{j} + 2\mathbf{k})$$

is the most general vector orthogonal to $\mathbf{a}$ and $\mathbf{b}$, where c_1 is arbitrary. In order that $\mathbf{c}$ be a unit vector we require

$$c^2 = 1 = \mathbf{c}.\mathbf{c} = c_1^2(1 + 9 + 4) = 14c_1^2,$$

i.e. $c_1 = \pm 1/\sqrt{14}$. The required vector is therefore

$$\pm \frac{1}{\sqrt{14}}(\mathbf{i} - 3\mathbf{j} + 2\mathbf{k}). \qquad \square$$

Problem 1.21 Find the general vector which is orthogonal to $\mathbf{a}$ and coplanar with $\mathbf{a}$ and $\mathbf{b}$, where $\mathbf{a}$ and $\mathbf{b}$ are as in Problem 1.20.

Solution. Let $\mathbf{d}$ be the required vector. Since it is coplanar with $\mathbf{a}$ and $\mathbf{b}$, we can write $\mathbf{d} = l\mathbf{a} + m\mathbf{b}$, for some real numbers l and m. Also, $\mathbf{d}$ is to be orthogonal to $\mathbf{a}$, and therefore

$$0 = \mathbf{d}.\mathbf{a} = (l\mathbf{a} + m\mathbf{b}).\mathbf{a} = la^2 + m\mathbf{b}.\mathbf{a}.$$

But $\quad a^2 = \mathbf{a}.\mathbf{a} = 8^2 + 2^2 + (-1)^2 = 69, \quad \mathbf{b}.\mathbf{a} = 24 - 2 + 3 = 25,$
giving
$$m = -69l/25.$$

Thus $\quad \mathbf{d} = l\left(\mathbf{a} - \frac{69}{25}\mathbf{b}\right) = \frac{l}{25}(25\mathbf{a} - 69\mathbf{b}) = p(\mathbf{i} - 17\mathbf{j} - 26\mathbf{k}),$

where $p = -7l/25$ is arbitrary. $\qquad \square$

Problem 1.22 Prove that if a tetrahedron has two pairs of mutually perpendicular opposite edges, then the third pair of opposite edges are also mutually perpendicular.

Solution. Let the vertices of the tetrahedron be O, A, B, C, and suppose that we are given: OA is perpendicular to BC, OB is perpendicular to CA. We wish to prove that OC is perpendicular to AB.

Let $\mathbf{a} = OA$, $\mathbf{b} = OB$, $\mathbf{c} = OC$. Then $AB = \mathbf{b} - \mathbf{a}$, $BC = \mathbf{c} - \mathbf{b}$, $CA = \mathbf{a} - \mathbf{c}$. The given relations are

11

$$\mathbf{a}.(\mathbf{c}-\mathbf{b}) = 0, \quad \mathbf{b}.(\mathbf{a}-\mathbf{c}) = 0.$$

Adding,
$$\mathbf{a}.\mathbf{c}-\mathbf{b}.\mathbf{c} = 0,$$

whence
$$\mathbf{c}.(\mathbf{b}-\mathbf{a}) = 0,$$

which proves that OC is perpendicular to AB. ☐

Problem 1.23 Four forces, $a(\mathbf{i}+\frac{3}{2}\mathbf{j}-\mathbf{k})$, $6a(\mathbf{j}+4\mathbf{k})$, $a(10\mathbf{i}-\mathbf{j}-12\mathbf{k})$, $-a\mathbf{i}$, act simultaneously on a particle P, a being a constant. Prove that if P moves in a straight line from the point $A(1,0,0)$ to the point $B(2,3,-1)$, the total work done by the forces is $37a/2$ units.

Solution. When a constant force $\mathbf{F}$ acts on a particle which moves along a straight line-segment AB, the work done by $\mathbf{F}$ is, by definition, $(F\cos\theta)AB = \mathbf{F}.\mathbf{AB}$, where θ is the angle between the directions of $\mathbf{F}$ and $\mathbf{AB}$. Thus, if we denote the given forces respectively by $\mathbf{F}_1, \mathbf{F}_2, \mathbf{F}_3, \mathbf{F}_4$, we get for the total work done

$$W = \mathbf{F}_1.\mathbf{AB}+\mathbf{F}_2.\mathbf{AB}+\mathbf{F}_3.\mathbf{AB}+\mathbf{F}_4.\mathbf{AB}$$
$$= \mathbf{R}.\mathbf{AB}, \qquad (1.14)$$

where $\mathbf{R}$ is the resultant of the forces $\mathbf{F}_i$, that is,

$$\mathbf{R} = \sum \mathbf{F}_i = a(10\mathbf{i}+\tfrac{13}{2}\mathbf{j}+11\mathbf{k}).$$

But $\mathbf{AB} = \mathbf{i}+3\mathbf{j}-\mathbf{k}$, and so we find from (1.14),

$$W = a(10+\tfrac{39}{2}-11) = \tfrac{37}{2}a \text{ units.}$$

1.6 Geometry of Lines and Planes The (vector) *equation* of a locus, such as a straight line or a plane, is an equation satisfied by the position vectors of all points on the locus and only these points.

Problem 1.24 Find the equation of the straight line through the points $A(\mathbf{a})$ and $B(\mathbf{b})$.

Solution. The notation $A(\mathbf{a})$ is used for the point A whose position vector relative to the origin is $\mathbf{a}$. Let $P(\mathbf{r})$ be a general point on the line (Fig. 1.6).

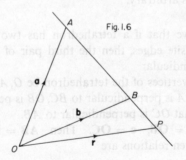

Fig. 1.6

12

Then the vectors **AP** and **AB** are parallel (in the same or opposite senses), so that we have

$$\mathbf{r} - \mathbf{a} = t(\mathbf{b} - \mathbf{a}) \qquad (1.15)$$

for some real number t. As the parameter t varies from $-\infty$ to $+\infty$, in (1.15), we get the position vector $P(\mathbf{r})$ of every point on the line, and no other point. Thus the required equation is

$$\mathbf{r} = \mathbf{a} + t(\mathbf{b} - \mathbf{a}), \qquad -\infty < t < \infty. \qquad \square \quad (1.16)$$

Problem 1.25 Find the equation of the straight line through the point $A(\mathbf{a})$ and parallel to the vector $\mathbf{d}$.

Solution. Let $B(\mathbf{b})$ be the point on the given line such that $\mathbf{d} = \mathbf{b} - \mathbf{a}$. Then, by Problem 1.24, the required equation can be written in the form (1.16), i.e.

$$\mathbf{r} = \mathbf{a} + t\mathbf{d}, \qquad -\infty < t < \infty. \qquad \square \quad (1.17)$$

Problem 1.26 Express (i) in vector form, (ii) in cartesian coordinate form, the equation of the straight line l which passes through the point $A(1, -1, 6)$ and is parallel to BC, where B and C are the points $(2, 1, 0)$ and $(-3, 2, -4)$, respectively. Show that the point $D(-9, 1, -2)$ lies on l.

Solution. (i) We have $\mathbf{BC} = -5\mathbf{i} + \mathbf{j} - 4\mathbf{k}$, and the vector equation of l is

$$\mathbf{r} = \mathbf{i} - \mathbf{j} + 6\mathbf{k} + t(-5\mathbf{i} + \mathbf{j} - 4\mathbf{k}),$$

or
$$\mathbf{r} = (1 - 5t)\mathbf{i} + (t - 1)\mathbf{j} + (6 - 4t)\mathbf{k}, \qquad -\infty < t < \infty. \qquad (1.18)$$

(ii) The last equation is equivalent to the three scalar equations

$$x = 1 - 5t, \quad y = -1 + t, \quad z = 6 - 4t,$$

where we have put $\mathbf{r} = x\mathbf{i} + y\mathbf{j} + z\mathbf{k}$. Elimination of t gives

$$\frac{x - 1}{-5} = \frac{y + 1}{1} = \frac{z - 6}{-4},$$

which is in the standard cartesian form for the equation of a straight line. It should be noted that in this form the denominators $(-5, 1, -4)$ are proportional to the direction cosines $(-5/\sqrt{42}, 1/\sqrt{42}, -4/\sqrt{42})$ of a vector, **BC**, which is parallel to the line.

The point $D(-9, 1, -2)$ lies on l if (1.18) becomes an identity for some value of t, when $\mathbf{r}$ is replaced by $-9\mathbf{i} + \mathbf{j} - 2\mathbf{k}$. Comparison of coefficients of $\mathbf{i}$ on the two sides shows that t must be equal to 2, and we find that the equation is indeed an identity for this value of t. $\qquad \square$

Problem 1.27 Find the equation of the plane p which contains the point $A(4\mathbf{i} - 3\mathbf{j} + \mathbf{k})$ and is parallel to the two vectors $\mathbf{b} = 3\mathbf{i} + 2\mathbf{j} + 2\mathbf{k}, \mathbf{c} = \mathbf{i} - \mathbf{j} - 4\mathbf{k}$.

Solution. Let A be chosen as initial point for the two vectors $\mathbf{b}$ and $\mathbf{c}$.

If P is a point in p, then

$$\mathbf{AP} = s\mathbf{b} + t\mathbf{c} = (3s+t)\mathbf{i} + (2s-t)\mathbf{j} + (2s-4t)\mathbf{k},$$

where $-\infty < s < \infty$, $-\infty < t < \infty$. Thus, the position vector of P relative to the origin is

$$\mathbf{r} = \mathbf{OP} = \mathbf{OA} + \mathbf{AP}$$
$$= (4+3s+t)\mathbf{i} + (2s-t-3)\mathbf{j} + (1+2s-4t)\mathbf{k}. \qquad \square$$

We note that the general form for the equation of a plane containing the point $A(\mathbf{a})$, and parallel to two (non-parallel) vectors $\mathbf{b}$ and $\mathbf{c}$, is $\mathbf{r} = \mathbf{a} + s\mathbf{b} + t\mathbf{c}$.

Problem 1.28 Show that the vector equation of a plane may be written in the scalar product form

$$\mathbf{r}.\mathbf{n} = q, \qquad (1.19)$$

where $\mathbf{n}$ is any vector normal to the plane and q is a constant. Show also that the perpendicular distance from the origin to the plane is $|q|/n$.

Solution. Let N be the foot of the perpendicular from the origin O to the plane, π say (Fig. 1.7). If P is a point in π, then NP is perpendicular to ON.

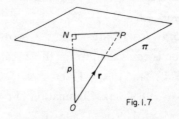

Fig. 1.7

Suppose first that $\mathbf{n}$ has the direction of $\mathbf{ON}$ (and not $\mathbf{NO}$). Then $\mathbf{ON} = p\hat{\mathbf{n}}$, where p is the perpendicular distance from O to π, and so $\mathbf{NP} = \mathbf{r} - p\hat{\mathbf{n}}$. Therefore

$$(\mathbf{r} - p\hat{\mathbf{n}}).\mathbf{n} = 0,$$

i.e.
$$\mathbf{r}.\mathbf{n} = pn = q,$$

where q is a constant. We note that q is positive since p and n are positive, and that $p = q/n$ as required.

If $\mathbf{n}$ has the direction $\mathbf{NO}$, then the above derivation is again valid if we replace $\mathbf{n}$ by $-\mathbf{n}$. The magnitude n is unchanged, and therefore $\mathbf{r}.\mathbf{n} = -np = q$, where the constant q is now negative, and $p = -q/n = |q|/n$ as before. $\qquad \square$

Problem 1.29 Find the vector equation of the plane through the point

14

$(1, 2, 0)$ and normal to the vector $\mathbf{n} = 2\mathbf{i} - 5\mathbf{j} + \mathbf{k}$. Determine (i) its distance from the origin, (ii) whether the perpendicular $\mathbf{ON}$ from the origin to the plane is in the same or opposite direction to $\mathbf{n}$, (iii) whether the plane passes through the point $A(3, 1, -9)$, (iv) the cartesian equation of the plane.

Solution. The vector equation must be of the form

$$\mathbf{r} \cdot (2\mathbf{i} - 5\mathbf{j} + \mathbf{k}) = q.$$

But the point $\mathbf{i} + 2\mathbf{j}$ lies on the plane, and so we must have

$$(\mathbf{i} + 2\mathbf{j}) \cdot (2\mathbf{i} - 5\mathbf{j} + \mathbf{k}) = q,$$

whence $q = -8$. Thus the required equation is

$$\mathbf{r} \cdot (2\mathbf{i} - 5\mathbf{j} + \mathbf{k}) = -8. \qquad (1.20)$$

(i) Since $n = \sqrt{30}$, the perpendicular distance from O to the plane is $|-8|/\sqrt{30} = 8/\sqrt{30}$.

(ii) Because q is negative, $\mathbf{ON}$ is in the opposite direction to $\mathbf{n}$.

(iii) The equation of the plane is satisfied when we substitute $3\mathbf{i} + \mathbf{j} - 9\mathbf{k}$ for $\mathbf{r}$, and so the point $A(3, 1, -9)$ lies on the plane.

(iv) Put $\mathbf{r} = x\mathbf{i} + y\mathbf{j} + z\mathbf{k}$. Then (1.20) becomes

$$2x - 5y + z = -8,$$

which is the required cartesian equation. ◻

Problem 1.30 Express in vector form the equation of the sphere of radius a, centre $\mathbf{c}$, and find the equation of the tangent plane at a point $\mathbf{b}$ on the sphere.

Solution. The point $P(\mathbf{r})$ is on the sphere if $|\mathbf{r} - \mathbf{c}| = a$, i.e. if

$$(\mathbf{r} - \mathbf{c})^2 = (\mathbf{r} - \mathbf{c}) \cdot (\mathbf{r} - \mathbf{c}) = a^2,$$

or $$r^2 - 2\mathbf{c} \cdot \mathbf{r} = a^2 - c^2.$$

The centre, C, has position vector $\mathbf{c}$ relative to the origin, and if B is the point on the sphere with position vector $\mathbf{b}$, then the vector $\mathbf{CB} = \mathbf{b} - \mathbf{c}$ is in the direction of the outward drawn normal at B. If $P(\mathbf{r})$ now denotes a point on the tangent plane at B, we have that BP is perpendicular to CB, i.e.

$$(\mathbf{r} - \mathbf{b}) \cdot (\mathbf{b} - \mathbf{c}) = 0.$$

It follows that this is the equation of the tangent plane at B. ◻

1.7 The Vector Product The *vector product* or *cross product* of two vectors $\mathbf{a}$ and $\mathbf{b}$ is defined to be the vector

$$\mathbf{a} \wedge \mathbf{b} = ab \sin \theta \, \hat{\mathbf{n}}, \qquad (1.21)$$

where θ $(0 \leqslant \theta \leqslant \pi)$ is the angle between the directions of $\mathbf{a}$ and $\mathbf{b}$, and $\hat{\mathbf{n}}$ is a unit vector normal to the plane of $\mathbf{a}$ and $\mathbf{b}$ (imagined to be drawn from a

15

common initial point). The sense of direction of $\hat{\mathbf{n}}$ is chosen so that a right-handed screw perpendicular to the plane of $\mathbf{a}$ and $\mathbf{b}$ would move in the direction $\hat{\mathbf{n}}$ if rotated in the sense which takes $\mathbf{a}$ into $\mathbf{b}$ (through the angle θ). Thus, in Fig. 1.4, if $\mathbf{a}$ and $\mathbf{b}$ lie in the plane of the diagram, then $\mathbf{a}\wedge\mathbf{b}$ (pronounced 'a cross b') is directed away from the reader and into the paper. The vector product of two non-zero vectors vanishes when, and only when, they are parallel (in the same or opposite directions).

The following laws are evident:

(i) $\mathbf{a}\wedge\mathbf{b} = -\mathbf{b}\wedge\mathbf{a}$,

(ii) $\mathbf{i}\wedge\mathbf{i} = \mathbf{j}\wedge\mathbf{j} = \mathbf{k}\wedge\mathbf{k} = 0$,

(iii) $\mathbf{i}\wedge\mathbf{j} = -\mathbf{j}\wedge\mathbf{i} = \mathbf{k}, \quad \mathbf{j}\wedge\mathbf{k} = -\mathbf{k}\wedge\mathbf{j} = \mathbf{i}, \quad \mathbf{k}\wedge\mathbf{i} = -\mathbf{i}\wedge\mathbf{k} = \mathbf{j}$,

(iv) $(m\mathbf{a})\wedge(n\mathbf{b}) = mn(\mathbf{a}\wedge\mathbf{b})$, where m and n are any real numbers.

It may also be proved that

(v) $\mathbf{a}\wedge(\mathbf{b}+\mathbf{c}) = \mathbf{a}\wedge\mathbf{b}+\mathbf{a}\wedge\mathbf{c}$,

(vi) $(\mathbf{a}+\mathbf{b})\wedge\mathbf{c} = \mathbf{a}\wedge\mathbf{c}+\mathbf{b}\wedge\mathbf{c}$.

Problem 1.31 Find $\mathbf{a}\wedge\mathbf{b}$, if $\mathbf{a} = 2\mathbf{i}+3\mathbf{j}-\mathbf{k}$, $\mathbf{b} = 3\mathbf{i}-2\mathbf{j}+2\mathbf{k}$.
Solution. We have

$$\mathbf{a}\wedge\mathbf{b} = (2\mathbf{i}+3\mathbf{j}-\mathbf{k})\wedge(3\mathbf{i}-2\mathbf{j}+2\mathbf{k})$$

$$= (2)(3)\mathbf{i}\wedge\mathbf{i}+(2)(-2)\mathbf{i}\wedge\mathbf{j}+(2)(2)\mathbf{i}\wedge\mathbf{k}+\ldots+(-1)(2)\mathbf{k}\wedge\mathbf{k}, \quad \text{by (v), (vi),}$$

$$= -4\mathbf{k}-4\mathbf{j}-9\mathbf{k}+6\mathbf{i}-3\mathbf{j}-2\mathbf{i}, \quad \text{by (ii), (iii),}$$

$$= 4\mathbf{i}-7\mathbf{j}-13\mathbf{k}. \qquad \qquad \square$$

If $\mathbf{a} = a_1\mathbf{i}+a_2\mathbf{j}+a_3\mathbf{k}$, $\mathbf{b} = b_1\mathbf{i}+b_2\mathbf{j}+b_3\mathbf{k}$, then the method of the last problem gives

$$\mathbf{a}\wedge\mathbf{b} = (a_2 b_3 - a_3 b_2)\mathbf{i}+(a_3 b_1 - a_1 b_3)\mathbf{j}+(a_1 b_2 - a_2 b_1)\mathbf{k},$$

which is identical to the expansion of the 'formal determinant'

$$\mathbf{a}\wedge\mathbf{b} = \begin{vmatrix} \mathbf{i} & \mathbf{j} & \mathbf{k} \\ a_1 & a_2 & a_3 \\ b_1 & b_2 & b_3 \end{vmatrix}. \tag{1.22}$$

Problem 1.32 Use the vector product to find the angle between the vectors $\mathbf{a} = 6\mathbf{i}-3\mathbf{j}+\mathbf{k}$, $\mathbf{b} = 2\mathbf{i}+2\mathbf{j}-\mathbf{k}$.
Solution. The required angle is θ, where by (1.21)

$$|\mathbf{a}\wedge\mathbf{b}| = ab\sin\theta,$$

$\sin\theta$ being positive for $0 \leqslant \theta \leqslant \pi$. Now,

16

$$\mathbf{a} \wedge \mathbf{b} = \begin{vmatrix} \mathbf{i} & \mathbf{j} & \mathbf{k} \\ 6 & -3 & 1 \\ 2 & 2 & -1 \end{vmatrix}$$

$$= \begin{vmatrix} -3 & 1 \\ 2 & -1 \end{vmatrix} \mathbf{i} - \begin{vmatrix} 6 & 1 \\ 2 & -1 \end{vmatrix} \mathbf{j} + \begin{vmatrix} 6 & -3 \\ 2 & 2 \end{vmatrix} \mathbf{k}$$

$$= \mathbf{i} + 8\mathbf{j} + 18\mathbf{k},$$

and so $|\mathbf{a} \wedge \mathbf{b}| = \sqrt{389}$. Also, we find $a = \sqrt{46}$, $b = 3$. Therefore

$$\sin \theta = \frac{|\mathbf{a} \wedge \mathbf{b}|}{ab} = \frac{\sqrt{389}}{3\sqrt{46}} = 0.9693,$$

giving $\theta = 75° \, 46'$. This problem should be compared with Problem 1.19.
□

Problem 1.33 Verify that in general we do *not* have $(\mathbf{a} \wedge \mathbf{b}) \wedge \mathbf{c} = \mathbf{a} \wedge (\mathbf{b} \wedge \mathbf{c})$, by evaluating the two sides in the case $\mathbf{a} = 2\mathbf{i} + \mathbf{j} + \mathbf{k}$, $\mathbf{b} = \mathbf{i} - \mathbf{j} - \mathbf{k}$, $\mathbf{c} = \mathbf{i} + 2\mathbf{j}$.

Solution. By (1.22),

$$\mathbf{a} \wedge \mathbf{b} = \begin{vmatrix} \mathbf{i} & \mathbf{j} & \mathbf{k} \\ 2 & 1 & 1 \\ 1 & -1 & -1 \end{vmatrix} = 3\mathbf{j} - 3\mathbf{k},$$

and thus

$$(\mathbf{a} \wedge \mathbf{b}) \wedge \mathbf{c} = \begin{vmatrix} \mathbf{i} & \mathbf{j} & \mathbf{k} \\ 0 & 3 & -3 \\ 1 & 2 & 0 \end{vmatrix} = 6\mathbf{i} - 3\mathbf{j} - 3\mathbf{k}.$$

In like manner we find $\mathbf{b} \wedge \mathbf{c} = 2\mathbf{i} - \mathbf{j} + 3\mathbf{k}$, and so

$$\mathbf{a} \wedge (\mathbf{b} \wedge \mathbf{c}) = \begin{vmatrix} \mathbf{i} & \mathbf{j} & \mathbf{k} \\ 2 & 1 & 1 \\ 2 & -1 & 3 \end{vmatrix} = 4\mathbf{i} - 4\mathbf{j} - 4\mathbf{k}.$$

Thus $(\mathbf{a} \wedge \mathbf{b}) \wedge \mathbf{c} \not\equiv \mathbf{a} \wedge (\mathbf{b} \wedge \mathbf{c})$; *c.f.* (2.13) and (2.14).
□

Definition Suppose that a rigid body rotates about a fixed axis parallel to a vector **d**. The rotation is said to be *positive* with respect to **d** if it is in the sense that would cause a right-handed screw along the axis to move in the direction **d**. More generally, a point is said to describe a *positive* circuit about a directed line, with direction **d**, if it makes a circuit in the sense of a positive rotation with respect to **d**. (Fig. 1.8).

Problem 1.34 Find the *vector area* of the triangle with vertices $A(\mathbf{a})$, $B(\mathbf{b})$, $C(\mathbf{c})$, taken in that order.

Fig. I.8

Solution. The *vector area* is the vector **v** whose magnitude is equal to the area of the triangle ABC, and whose direction is that of the unit normal $\hat{\mathbf{n}}$ to the plane ABC, the sense of $\hat{\mathbf{n}}$ being such that the vertices are encountered in the cyclic order A, B, C in a positive circuit of the triangle with respect to $\hat{\mathbf{n}}$. The area ABC is

$$|\mathbf{v}| = \tfrac{1}{2}AB . AC \sin BAC = \tfrac{1}{2}|\mathbf{AB}\wedge \mathbf{AC}|,$$

and the direction $\hat{\mathbf{n}}$ is that of the vector product $\mathbf{AB}\wedge \mathbf{AC}$ (Fig. 1.9).

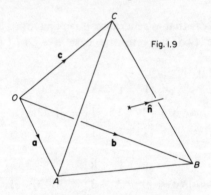

Fig. I.9

Therefore, **v** is given in magnitude and direction by

$$\mathbf{v} = \tfrac{1}{2}\mathbf{AB}\wedge \mathbf{AC} = \tfrac{1}{2}[(\mathbf{b}-\mathbf{a})\wedge (\mathbf{c}-\mathbf{a})]$$
$$= \tfrac{1}{2}(\mathbf{b}\wedge \mathbf{c}+\mathbf{c}\wedge \mathbf{a}+\mathbf{a}\wedge \mathbf{b}). \qquad \square$$

Definition The *vector moment* of a force **F** about the point P is the vector

$$\mathbf{M} = \mathbf{r}\wedge \mathbf{F}, \qquad (1.23)$$

where **r** is the position vector relative to P of any point Q on the line of action of **F** (Fig. 1.10).

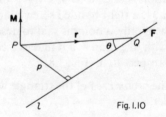

Fig. I.10

18

Problem 1.35 Prove that the magnitude of **M** is $M = pF$, where p is the perpendicular distance from P to the line of action, l, of **F**, and hence that **M** is independent of the particular choice of Q on l.

Solution. By definition of the vector product,

$$M = rF \sin \theta = pF,$$

where θ is the angle between **r** and **F**. This is clearly independent of the position of Q on l. Furthermore, the direction of $\mathbf{M} = \mathbf{r} \wedge \mathbf{F}$ is normal to the plane of P and l, the sense being such that **F** would induce a positive rotation with respect to **M** in a rigid body free to rotate about an axis parallel to **M** through P. It follows that the direction of **M** is also independent of the position of Q on l.

An alternative, vectorial, proof is possible. Let Q' be any point on l, and let $\mathbf{PQ'} = \mathbf{r'}$. We shall show that **M** in (1.23) is unchanged when Q is replaced by Q', i.e. when **r** is replaced by **r'**. We have that $\mathbf{QQ'} = k\mathbf{F}$, for some real number k. Thus,

$$\mathbf{r'} = \mathbf{PQ} + \mathbf{QQ'} = \mathbf{r} + k\mathbf{F},$$

therefore $\qquad\qquad \mathbf{r'} \wedge \mathbf{F} = (\mathbf{r} + k\mathbf{F}) \wedge \mathbf{F} = \mathbf{r} \wedge \mathbf{F},$

which was to be proved. $\qquad\qquad\qquad\qquad\qquad\qquad\qquad\qquad\qquad\qquad$ □

Problem 1.36 Forces of magnitude 3, 4 and 5 units, respectively, act on a triangular lamina at its vertices $A(1,0,0), B(0,1,0), C(0,0,1)$ and are directed along the edges AB, BC, CA. Find the sum of the moments of the forces about the point $D(2,0,1)$.

Solution. Denote the forces in the order given by $\mathbf{F}_1, \mathbf{F}_2, \mathbf{F}_3$. Then

$$\mathbf{F}_1 = 3\widehat{\mathbf{AB}}, \quad \mathbf{F}_2 = 4\widehat{\mathbf{BC}}, \quad \mathbf{F}_3 = 5\widehat{\mathbf{CA}}.$$

But $\qquad \mathbf{AB} = -\mathbf{i} + \mathbf{j}, \quad \mathbf{BC} = -\mathbf{j} + \mathbf{k}, \quad \mathbf{CA} = \mathbf{i} - \mathbf{k},$

$$\widehat{\mathbf{AB}} = \frac{1}{\sqrt{2}}(-\mathbf{i} + \mathbf{j}), \quad \widehat{\mathbf{BC}} = \frac{1}{\sqrt{2}}(-\mathbf{j} + \mathbf{k}), \quad \widehat{\mathbf{CA}} = \frac{1}{\sqrt{2}}(\mathbf{i} - \mathbf{k}).$$

Also $\quad \mathbf{DA} = -\mathbf{i} - \mathbf{k}, \quad \mathbf{DB} = -2\mathbf{i} + \mathbf{j} - \mathbf{k}, \quad \mathbf{DC} = -2\mathbf{i}.$

We thus find that the sum of the moments of the three forces about D is

$$\mathbf{DA} \wedge \mathbf{F}_1 + \mathbf{DB} \wedge \mathbf{F}_2 + \mathbf{DC} \wedge \mathbf{F}_3 = \frac{3}{\sqrt{2}}(\mathbf{i} + \mathbf{j} - \mathbf{k}) + \frac{4}{\sqrt{2}}(2\mathbf{j} + 2\mathbf{k}) + \frac{5}{\sqrt{2}}(-2\mathbf{j})$$

$$= \frac{1}{\sqrt{2}}(3\mathbf{i} + \mathbf{j} + 5\mathbf{k}),$$

on evaluating the vector products.

Alternatively, we might first have replaced the two forces acting through any vertex by their resultant acting through that vertex. $\qquad\qquad$ □

19

Problem 1.37   Show that the velocity of a particle P in a rigid body which rotates with *angular velocity* $\boldsymbol{\omega}$ about an axis through a fixed point O is $\mathbf{v} = \boldsymbol{\omega} \wedge \mathbf{r}$, where $\mathbf{r} = \mathbf{OP}$.

Solution. The *angular velocity vector* is defined as follows. Let $\hat{\mathbf{a}}$ be a unit vector parallel to the axis of rotation, such that the rotation is positive with respect to $\hat{\mathbf{a}}$. If ω is the angular speed of rotation (in radians per unit time), then by definition the angular velocity is $\boldsymbol{\omega} = \omega \hat{\mathbf{a}}$.

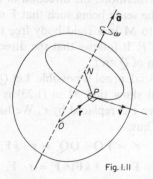

Fig. 1.11

Let N be the centre of the circular path followed by P (Fig. 1.11). The velocity of P at any instant has magnitude $NP . \omega = (r \sin NOP)\omega$, and its direction is perpendicular to the plane NOP in the same sense as $\boldsymbol{\omega} \wedge \mathbf{r}$. Therefore $\mathbf{v}$ and $\boldsymbol{\omega} \wedge \mathbf{r}$ agree in magnitude and direction, and so $\mathbf{v} = \boldsymbol{\omega} \wedge \mathbf{r}$.

Problem 1.38   A rigid body is rotating with angular speed 5 rad/s about an axis in the direction of the vector $2\mathbf{i}+\mathbf{j}$ through the point $A(0, 1, -4)$. Find the velocity of the particle at the point $B(1, 4, 1)$.

Solution. The unit vector in the direction of the axis of rotation is $\hat{\mathbf{a}} = (1/\sqrt{5})(2\mathbf{i}+\mathbf{j})$, and the angular velocity vector is therefore

$$\boldsymbol{\omega} = 5(1/\sqrt{5})(2\mathbf{i}+\mathbf{j}) = \sqrt{5}(2\mathbf{i}+\mathbf{j}).$$

The position vector of the point B relative to the point A on the axis is $\mathbf{AB} = \mathbf{i}+3\mathbf{j}+5\mathbf{k}$, and the velocity at B is

$$\boldsymbol{\omega} \wedge \mathbf{AB} = \sqrt{5}(2\mathbf{i}+\mathbf{j}) \wedge (\mathbf{i}+3\mathbf{j}+5\mathbf{k})$$
$$= 5\sqrt{5}(\mathbf{i}-2\mathbf{j}+\mathbf{k}),$$

(units of length per second). □

EXERCISES

1.   If $\mathbf{a} = \mathbf{i}-\mathbf{j}-\mathbf{k}$, $\mathbf{b} = 2\mathbf{i}+3\mathbf{j}+7\mathbf{k}$, $\mathbf{c} = \mathbf{j}-3\mathbf{k}$, find the following vectors: $\mathbf{a}+\mathbf{b}$, $\mathbf{a}-2\mathbf{b}$, $\mathbf{b}+2(\mathbf{c}-\mathbf{a})$. What is the terminal point of the vector $\mathbf{a}-2\mathbf{b}$ if $(0, 1, 1)$ is its initial point?

2. If the unit vectors $\mathbf{i}, \mathbf{j}$ represent displacements 150 km eastwards and 150 km northwards respectively, what is the vector that represents the displacement 300 km southwest? An aircraft flies 300 km southwest, and then 150 km in the direction 30° west of north. Calculate the distance and direction of its final position from its starting point.

3. A triangle has its vertices at the points A, B, C, whose position vectors relative to the origin are $\mathbf{a}, \mathbf{b}, \mathbf{c}$, respectively. Find the position vectors, relative to the origin, of the mid-point D of BC, and the point G which divides AD in the ratio $2:1$. Deduce that G lies on each of the three lines from a vertex to the mid-point of the opposite side. What geometrical theorem does this prove?

4. If $\mathbf{a}, \mathbf{b}, \mathbf{c}$ are the vectors given in Exercise 5, below, find the magnitudes of $\mathbf{a}, 2\mathbf{b} - \mathbf{c}, \mathbf{a} + 2\mathbf{b} - \mathbf{c}$. Find also (i) the direction cosines of $\mathbf{a} + 2\mathbf{b} - \mathbf{c}$; (ii) the unit vector in this direction.

5. Determine which (if any) sets of three different vectors selected from the following are linearly dependent:
$$\mathbf{a} = 2\mathbf{i} + \mathbf{j} - \mathbf{k}, \quad \mathbf{b} = \mathbf{i} - \mathbf{j} - 2\mathbf{k}, \quad \mathbf{c} = \mathbf{i} + 3\mathbf{k}, \quad \mathbf{d} = \mathbf{i} + 2\mathbf{j} + \mathbf{k}.$$

6. If $\mathbf{a} = \mathbf{i} + \mathbf{j} - \mathbf{k}, \mathbf{b} = 3\mathbf{i} - 3\mathbf{j} + \mathbf{k}$, find the angle between the vectors $\mathbf{a} - \mathbf{b}$ and $\mathbf{a} + \mathbf{b}$ using (i) the scalar product; (ii) the vector product.

7. Find the vector equations of the straight line AB and the plane ABC, where A, B, C are the points in Exercise 9, below. Give also the corresponding rectangular cartesian forms.

8. Find the equation of the line of intersection of the planes $\mathbf{r} \cdot (\mathbf{i} - \mathbf{j}) = 1$, $\mathbf{r} \cdot (2\mathbf{i} + \mathbf{j} + \mathbf{k}) = 2$.

9. A quadrilateral has its vertices at the points $A(1, 0, 1)$, $B(2, -1. 3)$, $C(0, 1, 2)$, $D(-1, 2, 2)$, and forces of magnitudes $3, 3, 2$ act along the (directed) sides AD, CB, CD respectively. Find the resultant of the forces, and also the vector sum of the moments about (i) the origin; (ii) the point D.

10. A rigid body is rotating about an axis through the origin. If the particle instantaneously at the point $(2, 0, 1)$ has velocity $2\mathbf{i} + 3\mathbf{j} - 4\mathbf{k}$, while that at the point $(0, 3, -1)$ has velocity $-8\mathbf{i} + \mathbf{j} + 3\mathbf{k}$, find the angular speed of rotation and the direction of the axis.

Chapter 2

Products of More Than Two Vectors

2.1 The Scalar Triple Product   The product $\mathbf{a} \cdot (\mathbf{b} \wedge \mathbf{c})$ is a scalar, called the *scalar triple product* of $\mathbf{a}$, $\mathbf{b}$ and $\mathbf{c}$. It has a simple geometrical interpretation. Take any point O as origin, and let A, B and C be points such that $\mathbf{OA} = \mathbf{a}$, $\mathbf{OB} = \mathbf{b}$, $\mathbf{OC} = \mathbf{c}$. Construct the parallelepiped with OA, OB and OC as concurrent edges (Fig. 2.1).

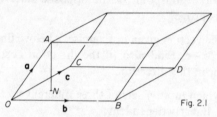

Fig. 2.1

In the diagram it is assumed that $\mathbf{a}$ makes an acute angle with $\mathbf{b} \wedge \mathbf{c}$, (in which case $\mathbf{a}, \mathbf{b}, \mathbf{c}$, in that order, are said to form a *right-handed* system). If N is the foot of the perpendicular from A to the plane BOC, and we denote the unit vector parallel to $\mathbf{NA}$ by $\hat{\mathbf{n}}$, then $\mathbf{b} \wedge \mathbf{c} = |\mathbf{b} \wedge \mathbf{c}| \hat{\mathbf{n}}$. Therefore

$$\mathbf{a} \cdot (\mathbf{b} \wedge \mathbf{c}) = \mathbf{a} \cdot \hat{\mathbf{n}} |\mathbf{b} \wedge \mathbf{c}|. \tag{2.1}$$

But $|\mathbf{b} \wedge \mathbf{c}| = OB \cdot OC \sin BOC$ is the area of the base parallelogram and $\mathbf{a} \cdot \hat{\mathbf{n}}$ is the perpendicular height of the solid figure. Hence the volume V of the figure is the scalar triple product (2.1).

If $\mathbf{a}$ makes an obtuse angle with $\mathbf{b} \wedge \mathbf{c}$ (the system $\mathbf{a}, \mathbf{b}, \mathbf{c}$ being *left-handed*), then the product $\mathbf{a} \cdot (\mathbf{b} \wedge \mathbf{c})$ is negative and equal to $-V$. When the three given vectors are coplanar, their scalar triple product vanishes, since $V = 0$. In particular, this is the case when two of the vectors are equal or are parallel.

By taking the other faces containing O, in turn, as base, we obtain two other scalar triple products which are each equal to V, and hence find that

$$\mathbf{a} \cdot (\mathbf{b} \wedge \mathbf{c}) = \mathbf{b} \cdot (\mathbf{c} \wedge \mathbf{a}) = \mathbf{c} \cdot (\mathbf{a} \wedge \mathbf{b}). \tag{2.2}$$

Furthermore, since the order of vectors occurring in a scalar product is immaterial, we have $\mathbf{a} \cdot (\mathbf{b} \wedge \mathbf{c}) = (\mathbf{b} \wedge \mathbf{c}) \cdot \mathbf{a}$, and hence find by (2.2) that each of the products there is equal also to

$$(\mathbf{a} \wedge \mathbf{b}) \cdot \mathbf{c} = (\mathbf{b} \wedge \mathbf{c}) \cdot \mathbf{a} = (\mathbf{c} \wedge \mathbf{a}) \cdot \mathbf{b}. \tag{2.3}$$

Property (2.2) is known as the *cyclic property*, while the equality of (2.2) and (2.3) demonstrates that the position of dot and cross is interchangeable.

Three vectors $\mathbf{a}, \mathbf{b}, \mathbf{c}$ may be written in any of six different orders, and in each ordering there can be formed two scalar triple products by placing the dot before the cross, or vice versa. The reader will easily confirm, using (i) on page 16, that there are only two distinct values for the products, and that these are equal and opposite.

Problem 2.1 Express $\mathbf{a}.(\mathbf{b} \wedge \mathbf{c})$ in component form.

Solution. Let

$$\mathbf{a} = a_1\mathbf{i} + a_2\mathbf{j} + a_3\mathbf{k}, \quad \mathbf{b} = b_1\mathbf{i} + b_2\mathbf{j} + b_3\mathbf{k}, \quad \mathbf{c} = c_1\mathbf{i} + c_2\mathbf{j} + c_3\mathbf{k}.$$

Then
$$\mathbf{a}.(\mathbf{b} \wedge \mathbf{c}) = (a_1\mathbf{i} + a_2\mathbf{j} + a_3\mathbf{k}).\begin{vmatrix} \mathbf{i} & \mathbf{j} & \mathbf{k} \\ b_1 & b_2 & b_3 \\ c_1 & c_2 & c_3 \end{vmatrix}$$

$$= a_1\begin{vmatrix} b_2 & b_3 \\ c_2 & c_3 \end{vmatrix} - a_2\begin{vmatrix} b_1 & b_3 \\ c_1 & c_3 \end{vmatrix} + a_3\begin{vmatrix} b_1 & b_2 \\ c_1 & c_2 \end{vmatrix}$$

$$= \begin{vmatrix} a_1 & a_2 & a_3 \\ b_1 & b_2 & b_3 \\ c_1 & c_2 & c_3 \end{vmatrix}. \tag{2.4}$$
$\square$

Problem 2.2 Evaluate
$$(8\mathbf{i} - 6\mathbf{j} + 4\mathbf{k}).\{(7\mathbf{i} - 11\mathbf{j} + 9\mathbf{k}) \wedge (-4\mathbf{i} + 3\mathbf{j} - 2\mathbf{k})\}.$$

Solution. The first vector is a multiple of the third, and as we have shown, the scalar triple product of three vectors vanishes when any two of the vectors are parallel. Thus the value is zero. Note that this also follows from the determinant form (2.4), since a determinant vanishes when two of its rows are proportional.
$\square$

Problem 2.3 Prove that the four points $A(2, 0, 1)$, $B(-1, 2, 3)$, $C(3, 2, 2)$, $D(3, -6, -3)$ lie in a plane.

Solution. An evident necessary and sufficient condition for the points to lie in a plane is that the vectors $\mathbf{AB}, \mathbf{AC}, \mathbf{AD}$ be coplanar. We have

$$\mathbf{AB} = -3\mathbf{i} + 2\mathbf{j} + 2\mathbf{k}, \quad \mathbf{AC} = \mathbf{i} + 2\mathbf{j} + \mathbf{k}, \quad \mathbf{AD} = \mathbf{i} - 6\mathbf{j} - 4\mathbf{k},$$

and therefore

$$\mathbf{AB}.(\mathbf{AC} \wedge \mathbf{AD}) = \begin{vmatrix} -3 & 2 & 2 \\ 1 & 2 & 1 \\ 1 & -6 & -4 \end{vmatrix} = -3(-2) - 2(-5) + 2(-8) = 0.$$

Thus $\mathbf{AB}, \mathbf{AC}$ and $\mathbf{AD}$ are coplanar and the points A, B, C, D lie in a plane.
$\square$

Let a force $\mathbf{F}$ act along a given line in a rigid body. The *moment of* $\mathbf{F}$

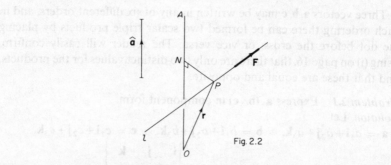

Fig. 2.2

about an axis OA is defined to be the component in the direction **OA** of the moment of **F** about O (Fig. 2.2). Thus, if P is any point on the line of action l, and $\mathbf{r} = \mathbf{OP}$, then the moment of **F** about O is $\mathbf{M} = \mathbf{r} \wedge \mathbf{F}$, and the moment about the axis OA is

$$m = \hat{\mathbf{a}}.\mathbf{M} = \hat{\mathbf{a}}.(\mathbf{r} \wedge \mathbf{F}), \tag{2.5}$$

where $\hat{\mathbf{a}}$ is the unit vector in the direction **OA**. The scalar m is independent of the point O on a given axis, since if we replace O by any other point O' on OA, and write $\mathbf{r}' = \mathbf{O'P}$, then we get for the scalar moment

$$m' = \hat{\mathbf{a}}.(\mathbf{r}' \wedge \mathbf{F}) = \hat{\mathbf{a}}.[(\mathbf{r} - \mathbf{OO'}) \wedge \mathbf{F}]$$
$$= \hat{\mathbf{a}}.(\mathbf{r} \wedge \mathbf{F}) = m,$$

since $\hat{\mathbf{a}}$ is parallel to **OO'**.

***Problem* 2.4** A force of magnitude 5 units acts along the line $\mathbf{r} = (3+s)\mathbf{i} - 2s\mathbf{j} + (1-2s)\mathbf{k}$ in the sense in which s is increasing. Find its moment about an axis in the direction of the vector $\mathbf{i} - \mathbf{k}$ through the point $A(1, 1, 2)$.

Solution. The line of action of the force, **F**, can be written

$$\mathbf{r} = 3\mathbf{i} + \mathbf{k} + s(\mathbf{i} - 2\mathbf{j} - 2\mathbf{k}), \tag{2.6}$$

which shows that it passes through the point $P(3, 0, 1)$ and is parallel to the unit vector $\frac{1}{3}(\mathbf{i} - 2\mathbf{j} - 2\mathbf{k})$. This unit vector is directed in the sense in which s increases, since a positive increment to s in (2.6) results in a displacement of the terminal point of **r** in the direction of the bracketed vector. Thus,

$$\mathbf{F} = \tfrac{5}{3}(\mathbf{i} - 2\mathbf{j} - 2\mathbf{k}).$$

The unit vector in the direction of the given axis is $\hat{\mathbf{a}} = (1/\sqrt{2})(\mathbf{i} - \mathbf{k})$, and so the required moment is

$$m = \hat{\mathbf{a}}.(\mathbf{AP} \wedge \mathbf{F}) = \frac{1}{\sqrt{2}}(\mathbf{i} - \mathbf{k}).[(2\mathbf{i} - \mathbf{j} - \mathbf{k}) \wedge \tfrac{5}{3}(\mathbf{i} - 2\mathbf{j} - 2\mathbf{k})]$$
$$= 5/\sqrt{2} \text{ units.} \qquad \square$$

24

Forces associated with particular lines of action are examples of *line-localized* vectors. The moment of a line-localized vector $\mathbf{F}$ about an axis depends only on the axis, the line of action and the vector $\mathbf{F}$. The angular velocity vector of a rigid body which rotates about a fixed point is another example of a line-localized vector.

Problem 2.5 Prove that (2.5) may also be written

$$m = \hat{\mathbf{a}} \cdot (\mathbf{r} \wedge \mathbf{F}'),$$

where $\mathbf{F}'$ is the vector component of $\mathbf{F}$ perpendicular to the plane OAP. Interpret this result.

Solution. Let $\mathbf{F} = \mathbf{F}' + \mathbf{F}''$, where $\mathbf{F}''$ is parallel to the plane OAP. Then

$$m = \hat{\mathbf{a}} \cdot (\mathbf{r} \wedge \mathbf{F}) = \hat{\mathbf{a}} \cdot [\mathbf{r} \wedge (\mathbf{F}' + \mathbf{F}'')] = \hat{\mathbf{a}} \cdot (\mathbf{r} \wedge \mathbf{F}'),$$

since $\hat{\mathbf{a}}$, $\mathbf{r}$ and $\mathbf{F}''$ are coplanar, all being parallel to the plane OAP.

The result shows that only the component of $\mathbf{F}$ normal to the plane OAP contributes to the moment about OA. Let N be the point on OA such that NP is perpendicular to OA. Since the axis may equally well be taken as NA, we have (see comments following (2.5)),

$$m = \hat{\mathbf{a}} \cdot (\mathbf{NP} \wedge \mathbf{F}'),$$

where $\hat{\mathbf{a}}$, $\mathbf{NP}$ and $\mathbf{F}'$ form a mutually orthogonal set. According as this set is right-handed or left-handed, m is positive or negative, and $|m|$ is the magnitude of the moment of $\mathbf{F}'$ about the point N.

We can regard m as a measure of the tendency of the force $\mathbf{F}$ to cause a rigid body to rotate about a fixed axis along OA, the rotation being positive when m is positive, and negative when m is negative. $\qquad \square$

2.2 Reciprocal Sets of Vectors
Problem 2.6 Let $\mathbf{a}, \mathbf{b}, \mathbf{c}$ be non-coplanar vectors, and let $\mathbf{r}$ be an arbitrary vector. Then $\mathbf{r}$ may evidently be expressed in the form

$$\mathbf{r} = l\mathbf{a} + m\mathbf{b} + n\mathbf{c}, \tag{2.7}$$

for some real numbers l, m, n. Find l, m, n in terms of $\mathbf{r}, \mathbf{a}, \mathbf{b}, \mathbf{c}$.

Solution. Since $\mathbf{b} \cdot (\mathbf{b} \wedge \mathbf{c}) = \mathbf{c} \cdot (\mathbf{b} \wedge \mathbf{c}) = 0$, we can eliminate $\mathbf{b}$ and $\mathbf{c}$ in (2.7) by forming the scalar product on each side with $\mathbf{b} \wedge \mathbf{c}$. Thus,

$$\mathbf{r} \cdot (\mathbf{b} \wedge \mathbf{c}) = l\mathbf{a} \cdot (\mathbf{b} \wedge \mathbf{c}), \quad \text{or} \quad l = \frac{\mathbf{r} \cdot (\mathbf{b} \wedge \mathbf{c})}{\mathbf{a} \cdot (\mathbf{b} \wedge \mathbf{c})},$$

where the denominator does not vanish since $\mathbf{a}, \mathbf{b}, \mathbf{c}$ are non-coplanar. By multiplying the two sides of (2.7) in turn by $\mathbf{c} \wedge \mathbf{a}$ and $\mathbf{a} \wedge \mathbf{b}$, forming the scalar product in each case, we similarly find m and n.

The results can be written concisely in the form

$$l = \mathbf{r} . \mathbf{a}', \quad m = \mathbf{r} . \mathbf{b}', \quad n = \mathbf{r} . \mathbf{c}',$$

where
$$\mathbf{a}' = \frac{\mathbf{b} \wedge \mathbf{c}}{\mathbf{a} . (\mathbf{b} \wedge \mathbf{c})}, \quad \mathbf{b}' = \frac{\mathbf{c} \wedge \mathbf{a}}{\mathbf{a} . (\mathbf{b} \wedge \mathbf{c})}, \quad \mathbf{c}' = \frac{\mathbf{a} \wedge \mathbf{b}}{\mathbf{a} . (\mathbf{b} \wedge \mathbf{c})}. \quad (2.8)$$

The set of vectors $\mathbf{a}', \mathbf{b}', \mathbf{c}'$ is said to be *reciprocal* to the set $\mathbf{a}, \mathbf{b}, \mathbf{c}$. ☐

***Problem* 2.7** Show that the set of vectors $\mathbf{i}, \mathbf{j}, \mathbf{k}$ is *self-reciprocal*.

Solution. Since $\mathbf{j} \wedge \mathbf{k} = \mathbf{i}$, we have that $\mathbf{i} . (\mathbf{j} \wedge \mathbf{k}) = 1$, and hence if $\mathbf{i}', \mathbf{j}', \mathbf{k}'$ is the set of vectors reciprocal to the set $\mathbf{i}, \mathbf{j}, \mathbf{k}$, then

$$\mathbf{i}' = \frac{\mathbf{j} \wedge \mathbf{k}}{\mathbf{i} . (\mathbf{j} \wedge \mathbf{k})} = \mathbf{i}.$$

Likewise we find that $\mathbf{j}' = \mathbf{j}$ and $\mathbf{k}' = \mathbf{k}$. Thus, the set $\mathbf{i}, \mathbf{j}, \mathbf{k}$ is reciprocal to itself, or *self-reciprocal*. ☐

***Problem* 2.8** Prove the relations

$$\mathbf{a} . \mathbf{a}' = \mathbf{b} . \mathbf{b}' = \mathbf{c} . \mathbf{c}' = 1, \quad (2.9)$$

$$\mathbf{a} . \mathbf{b}' = \mathbf{a}' . \mathbf{b} = \mathbf{b} . \mathbf{c}' = \mathbf{b}' . \mathbf{c} = \mathbf{c} . \mathbf{a}' = \mathbf{c}' . \mathbf{a} = 0. \quad (2.10)$$

Solution. By (2.8), we have

$$\mathbf{a} . \mathbf{a}' = \frac{\mathbf{a} . (\mathbf{b} \wedge \mathbf{c})}{\mathbf{a} . (\mathbf{b} \wedge \mathbf{c})} = 1,$$

and the two other relations in (2.9) are similarly proved, using the cyclic property of the scalar triple product. Again by (2.8),

$$\mathbf{a} . \mathbf{b}' = \frac{\mathbf{a} . (\mathbf{c} \wedge \mathbf{a})}{\mathbf{a} . (\mathbf{b} \wedge \mathbf{c})} = 0,$$

since the scalar triple product in the numerator contains the same vector twice. For precisely the same reason, the other five scalar products in (2.10) are found also to vanish. ☐

***Problem* 2.9** Prove that $\mathbf{a}', \mathbf{b}', \mathbf{c}'$ are non-coplanar, and hence that there is a set of vectors, $\mathbf{a}'', \mathbf{b}'', \mathbf{c}''$ say, reciprocal to $\mathbf{a}', \mathbf{b}', \mathbf{c}'$. Prove also that

$$\mathbf{a}'' = \mathbf{a}, \quad \mathbf{b}'' = \mathbf{b}, \quad \mathbf{c}'' = \mathbf{c}.$$

Solution. A direct vector proof is given in Problem 2.12. The following alternative argument, based on matrix theory, is instructive.

Let the rectangular components of $\mathbf{r}, \mathbf{a}, \mathbf{b}, \mathbf{c}$ be (x, y, z), (a_1, a_2, a_3), (b_1, b_2, b_3), (c_1, c_2, c_3), respectively, where $\mathbf{r}$ is an arbitrary vector. Equation (2.7) can be written in the matrix form

$$\begin{pmatrix} x \\ y \\ z \end{pmatrix} = \begin{pmatrix} a_1 & b_1 & c_1 \\ a_2 & b_2 & c_2 \\ a_3 & b_3 & c_3 \end{pmatrix} \begin{pmatrix} l \\ m \\ n \end{pmatrix}. \quad (2.11)$$

Let A denote the 3×3 matrix on the right; the condition that $\mathbf{a}, \mathbf{b}, \mathbf{c}$ are non-coplanar is that determinant $A \neq 0$. Thus, (2.11) can be solved uniquely for l, m, n in terms of x, y, z, giving

$$\begin{pmatrix} l \\ m \\ n \end{pmatrix} = A^{-1} \begin{pmatrix} x \\ y \\ z \end{pmatrix} = \begin{pmatrix} a'_1 & b'_1 & c'_1 \\ a'_2 & b'_2 & c'_2 \\ a'_3 & b'_3 & c'_3 \end{pmatrix} \begin{pmatrix} x \\ y \\ z \end{pmatrix}, \tag{2.12}$$

by comparison with expressions found for l, m, n in Problem 2.6. Thus we find that A^{-1} has the same form as A with each element primed. Now, $\mathbf{a}' . (\mathbf{b}' \wedge \mathbf{c}')$ is simply $\det . A^{-1}$, and by a standard result of determinant theory $(\det . A^{-1})(\det . A) = 1$, whence it follows that $\mathbf{a}' . (\mathbf{b}' \wedge \mathbf{c}') \neq 0$. Therefore, $\mathbf{a}', \mathbf{b}', \mathbf{c}'$ are non-coplanar, so that there is a set of vectors $\mathbf{a}'', \mathbf{b}'', \mathbf{c}''$ reciprocal to them.

The second part of the problem follows from the matrix identity $(A^{-1})^{-1} = A$.

The relations (2.9) and (2.10) may also be proved by the matrix method, and are the vector form of the identity $AA^{-1} = I$, where I denotes the 3×3 identity (or unit) matrix. □

2.3 The Vector Triple Product The *vector triple product* $\mathbf{a} \wedge (\mathbf{b} \wedge \mathbf{c})$ is a vector orthogonal both to $\mathbf{a}$ and to $\mathbf{b} \wedge \mathbf{c}$. It is parallel to any plane containing $\mathbf{b}$ and $\mathbf{c}$, since $\mathbf{b} \wedge \mathbf{c}$ is normal to such a plane. By expressing the two sides in rectangular component form, one may easily verify that

$$\mathbf{a} \wedge (\mathbf{b} \wedge \mathbf{c}) = (\mathbf{a} . \mathbf{c})\mathbf{b} - (\mathbf{a} . \mathbf{b})\mathbf{c}. \tag{2.13}$$

Consider also the vector triple product formed by bracketing, instead, the first pair of vectors on the left. We have, by (2.13),

$$(\mathbf{a} \wedge \mathbf{b}) \wedge \mathbf{c} = -\mathbf{c} \wedge (\mathbf{a} \wedge \mathbf{b}) = (\mathbf{c} . \mathbf{a})\mathbf{b} - (\mathbf{c} . \mathbf{b})\mathbf{a}. \tag{2.14}$$

Thus, the two vector triple products are quite different (*c.f.* Problem 1.33); one is coplanar with $\mathbf{b}$ and $\mathbf{c}$, and the other is coplanar with $\mathbf{b}$ and $\mathbf{a}$. However, the two expansions may be remembered by the same rule. On the right, the first term is the middle vector, $\mathbf{b}$, multiplied by the scalar product of the other two. The second (subtracted) term is the other bracketed vector in the triple product, multiplied by the scalar product of the remaining pair.

Problem 2.10 Prove that
$$(\mathbf{a} \wedge \mathbf{b}) . (\mathbf{c} \wedge \mathbf{d}) = (\mathbf{a} . \mathbf{c})(\mathbf{b} . \mathbf{d}) - (\mathbf{a} . \mathbf{d})(\mathbf{b} . \mathbf{c}).$$

Solution. Let $\mathbf{e} = \mathbf{c} \wedge \mathbf{d}$. Interchanging dot and cross we get
$$\begin{aligned}
(\mathbf{a} \wedge \mathbf{b}) . \mathbf{e} &= \mathbf{a} . (\mathbf{b} \wedge \mathbf{e}) = \mathbf{a} . [\mathbf{b} \wedge (\mathbf{c} \wedge \mathbf{d})] \\
&= \mathbf{a} . [(\mathbf{b} . \mathbf{d})\mathbf{c} - (\mathbf{b} . \mathbf{c})\mathbf{d}], \quad \text{by (2.13),} \\
&= (\mathbf{a} . \mathbf{c})(\mathbf{b} . \mathbf{d}) - (\mathbf{a} . \mathbf{d})(\mathbf{b} . \mathbf{c}). \quad\quad □
\end{aligned}$$

Problem 2.11 Prove that

$$(\mathbf{b} \wedge \mathbf{c}) . [(\mathbf{c} \wedge \mathbf{a}) \wedge (\mathbf{a} \wedge \mathbf{b})] \geqslant 0,$$

and that equality holds if and only if $\mathbf{a}, \mathbf{b}, \mathbf{c}$ are coplanar.

Solution. By (2.14), treating $\mathbf{a} \wedge \mathbf{b}$ as one vector,

$$(\mathbf{c} \wedge \mathbf{a}) \wedge (\mathbf{a} \wedge \mathbf{b}) = [\mathbf{c} . (\mathbf{a} \wedge \mathbf{b})]\mathbf{a} - [\mathbf{a} . (\mathbf{a} \wedge \mathbf{b})]\mathbf{c}$$
$$= [\mathbf{a} . (\mathbf{b} \wedge \mathbf{c})]\mathbf{a}, \tag{2.15}$$

since $\mathbf{a} . (\mathbf{a} \wedge \mathbf{b}) = 0$. On forming the scalar product on each side with $\mathbf{b} \wedge \mathbf{c}$, we find that the given expression is equal to $[\mathbf{a} . (\mathbf{b} \wedge \mathbf{c})]^2$, which is a strictly positive scalar unless $\mathbf{a} . (\mathbf{b} \wedge \mathbf{c}) = 0$, i.e. unless $\mathbf{a}, \mathbf{b}$ and $\mathbf{c}$ are coplanar, in which case the value of the scalar is zero. ☐

Problem 2.12 If $\mathbf{a}', \mathbf{b}', \mathbf{c}'$ is the set of vectors reciprocal to the non-coplanar set $\mathbf{a}, \mathbf{b}, \mathbf{c}$, prove that $\mathbf{a}' . (\mathbf{b}' \wedge \mathbf{c}') \neq 0$. Prove also that $\mathbf{a}, \mathbf{b}, \mathbf{c}$ is the set reciprocal to $\mathbf{a}', \mathbf{b}', \mathbf{c}'$ (*c.f.* Problem 2.9).

Solution. By definition, if k denotes $\mathbf{a} . (\mathbf{b} \wedge \mathbf{c})$,

$$\mathbf{b}' \wedge \mathbf{c}' = \frac{1}{k}(\mathbf{c} \wedge \mathbf{a}) \wedge \frac{1}{k}(\mathbf{a} \wedge \mathbf{b}) = \frac{1}{k}\mathbf{a}, \tag{2.16}$$

by (2.15). Thus,

$$\mathbf{a}' . (\mathbf{b}' \wedge \mathbf{c}') = \frac{1}{k}\mathbf{a}' . \mathbf{a} = \frac{1}{k}, \tag{2.17}$$

using (2.9). Thus, the expression on the left is not equal to zero.

For the second part, let $\mathbf{a}'', \mathbf{b}'', \mathbf{c}''$ be the set reciprocal to $\mathbf{a}, \mathbf{b}, \mathbf{c}$. Then

$$\mathbf{a}'' = \frac{\mathbf{b}' \wedge \mathbf{c}'}{\mathbf{a}' . (\mathbf{b}' \wedge \mathbf{c}')} = \mathbf{a},$$

by (2.16), (2.17). In like manner we find that $\mathbf{b}'' = \mathbf{b}$, $\mathbf{c}'' = \mathbf{c}$, and hence the set reciprocal to $\mathbf{a}', \mathbf{b}', \mathbf{c}'$ is $\mathbf{a}, \mathbf{b}, \mathbf{c}$. ☐

2.4 Further Geometrical Examples

Problem 2.13 Show that the condition that two non-parallel straight lines $\mathbf{r} = \mathbf{a} + s\mathbf{b}$, $\mathbf{r} = \mathbf{a}' + t\mathbf{b}'$ intersect is that $(\mathbf{a} - \mathbf{a}') . (\mathbf{b} \wedge \mathbf{b}') = 0$.

Solution. Suppose that the lines intersect at a point P. Let A, A' be the points on the respective lines with position vectors $\mathbf{a}$, $\mathbf{a}'$, relative to the origin. Then the vector $\mathbf{PA}$ is parallel to $\mathbf{b}$, since PA is a segment of the first line. Similarly, $\mathbf{PA'}$ is parallel to $\mathbf{b}'$, since PA' is a segment of the second line. Also, $\mathbf{A'A} = \mathbf{a} - \mathbf{a}'$, and since $\mathbf{PA}$, $\mathbf{PA'}$, $\mathbf{A'A}$ are coplanar, being the sides of a triangle, it follows that $(\mathbf{a} - \mathbf{a}') . (\mathbf{b} \wedge \mathbf{b}') = 0$.

This condition is also sufficient for the given non-parallel lines to intersect. For it implies that there is a plane through $A'A$ to which both

28

b and **b'** are parallel. Both the given lines lie in this plane, and since they are not parallel they must intersect. $\qquad\square$

Problem 2.14 Find the equation of the straight line which passes through the point with position vector **c** and meets both the skew lines $\mathbf{r} = \mathbf{a} + s\mathbf{b}, \mathbf{r} = \mathbf{a'} + t\mathbf{b'}$.

Solution. Skew lines are non-intersecting, non-parallel lines. Since the required line passes through the point with position vector **c**, its equation is of the form $\mathbf{r} = \mathbf{c} + u\mathbf{d}$, where u is a parameter and **d** is to be determined (to within a constant multiple). The conditions for this line to meet the two skew lines are (by Problem 2.13)

$$(\mathbf{a} - \mathbf{c}) \cdot (\mathbf{b} \wedge \mathbf{d}) = 0,$$
$$(\mathbf{a'} - \mathbf{c}) \cdot (\mathbf{b'} \wedge \mathbf{d}) = 0.$$

Interchanging dot and cross,

$$[(\mathbf{a} - \mathbf{c}) \wedge \mathbf{b}] \cdot \mathbf{d} = 0,$$
$$[(\mathbf{a'} - \mathbf{c}) \wedge \mathbf{b'}] \cdot \mathbf{d} = 0,$$

which shows that **d** is perpendicular to each of the square-bracketed expressions. Since **d** is determinate only to within a constant multiple, we may choose **d** to be the vector product of these expressions, whence the required line is given by

$$\mathbf{r} = \mathbf{c} + u[(\mathbf{a} - \mathbf{c}) \wedge \mathbf{b}] \wedge [(\mathbf{a'} - \mathbf{c}) \wedge \mathbf{b'}]. \qquad\square$$

Problem 2.15 Prove that the length of the common perpendicular to the skew lines $\mathbf{r} = \mathbf{a} + s\mathbf{b}, \mathbf{r} = \mathbf{a'} + t\mathbf{b'}$ is

$$\pm \frac{(\mathbf{a'} - \mathbf{a}) \cdot (\mathbf{b} \wedge \mathbf{b'})}{|\mathbf{b} \wedge \mathbf{b'}|},$$

the sign being chosen so as to make the value positive.

Solution. We first prove the existence of a unique common perpendicular. Let p denote the plane which contains the first line and is parallel to the second, and let p' denote the plane which contains the second line and is parallel to the first. These two planes are each parallel to **b** and **b'**, and hence to each other. Let PN be the direction of their common normal, where P is on p and N is on p'.

Allow P to vary along the first line. Then the locus of N is a straight line parallel to **b** on p', and meets the second line for just one position of P. In this position (Fig. 2.3), PN is the common perpendicular, and it is unique since any common perpendicular must satisfy all the conditions we have imposed on PN.

Since the points **a** and **a'** are on p and p' respectively, the perpendicular

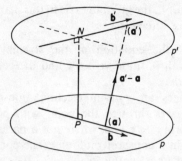

Fig 2.3

distance PN between the two planes is equal to the normal component of $\mathbf{a'}-\mathbf{a}$. Now, a normal vector is given by $\mathbf{b}\wedge\mathbf{b'}$, and hence the unit normal to the two planes is

$$\hat{\mathbf{n}} = \pm\frac{\mathbf{b}\wedge\mathbf{b'}}{|\mathbf{b}\wedge\mathbf{b'}|}. \tag{2.18}$$

Therefore, the length of the common perpendicular is

$$l = (\mathbf{a'}-\mathbf{a})\cdot\hat{\mathbf{n}},$$

where $\hat{\mathbf{n}}$ is given by (2.18), the sign being chosen so as to make l positive.

□

Problem 2.16   Find the equation of the plane of the triangle $A(\mathbf{a})$, $B(\mathbf{b})$, $C(\mathbf{c})$.

Solution. A normal vector to the plane is given by

$$\mathbf{n} = \mathbf{AB}\wedge\mathbf{AC} = (\mathbf{b}-\mathbf{a})\wedge(\mathbf{c}-\mathbf{a}) = \mathbf{b}\wedge\mathbf{c}+\mathbf{c}\wedge\mathbf{a}+\mathbf{a}\wedge\mathbf{b}, \tag{2.19}$$

and the equation of the plane must be of the form (1.19)

$$\mathbf{r}\cdot\mathbf{n} = q,$$

where q is to be determined. But the point A lies on the plane, and so

$$\mathbf{a}\cdot\mathbf{n} = q = \mathbf{a}\cdot(\mathbf{b}\wedge\mathbf{c}),$$

by (2.19). Hence the required equation is

$$\mathbf{r}\cdot(\mathbf{b}\wedge\mathbf{c}+\mathbf{c}\wedge\mathbf{a}+\mathbf{a}\wedge\mathbf{b}) = \mathbf{a}\cdot(\mathbf{b}\wedge\mathbf{c}). \qquad\square$$

A 'triangle' formed by arcs of great circles on a sphere is called a *spherical triangle*. In deriving formulae for such triangles (used in navigation, astronomy, etc.), it may be assumed that the sphere has unit radius.

Problem 2.17   A spherical triangle on a sphere of radius unity and centre O has vertices at A, B, C. If a, b, c denote the arc lengths of the sides

30

BC, CA, AB, then a, b, c are respectively equal to the angles $BOC, COA,$ AOB (measured in radians; Fig. 2.4). Prove the formulae

$$\frac{\sin A}{\sin a} = \frac{\sin B}{\sin b} = \frac{\sin C}{\sin c}, \qquad (2.20)$$

and $$\cos a = \cos b \cos c + \sin b \sin c \cos A,$$

with similar forms to the latter obtained by cyclic permutation of vertices and sides.

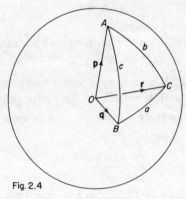

Fig. 2.4

Solution. Introduce vectors along the radii through the vertices: $\mathbf{OA} = \mathbf{p}$, $\mathbf{OB} = \mathbf{q}$, $\mathbf{OC} = \mathbf{r}$. These are unit vectors and therefore

$$|\mathbf{q} \wedge \mathbf{r}| = \sin BOC = \sin a, \quad |\mathbf{r} \wedge \mathbf{p}| = \sin b, \quad |\mathbf{p} \wedge \mathbf{q}| = \sin c, \qquad (2.21)$$

$$\mathbf{q} \cdot \mathbf{r} = \cos BOC = \cos a, \quad \mathbf{r} \cdot \mathbf{p} = \cos b, \quad \mathbf{p} \cdot \mathbf{q} = \cos c.$$

Now, the angle A is that between the diametral planes AOB, and AOC, and hence between their normals $\mathbf{p} \wedge \mathbf{r}$, $\mathbf{p} \wedge \mathbf{q}$. On taking moduli on both sides of the identity (*c.f.* (2.15))

$$(\mathbf{p} \wedge \mathbf{q}) \wedge (\mathbf{p} \wedge \mathbf{r}) = [\mathbf{p} \cdot (\mathbf{q} \wedge \mathbf{r})] \mathbf{p},$$

and using (2.21), we get

$$\sin b \sin c \sin A = |\mathbf{p} \cdot (\mathbf{q} \wedge \mathbf{r})|,$$

and by cyclic permutation of vertices and sides,

$$\sin c \sin a \sin B = |\mathbf{q} \cdot (\mathbf{r} \wedge \mathbf{p})|,$$

$$\sin a \sin b \sin C = |\mathbf{r} \cdot (\mathbf{p} \wedge \mathbf{q})|.$$

The right-hand sides of the last three equations are equal, and so must be the left-hand sides. Equations (2.20) follow immediately.

To prove the second set of formulae, consider the identity

$$(\mathbf{p} \wedge \mathbf{q}) \cdot (\mathbf{p} \wedge \mathbf{r}) = \mathbf{p} \cdot [\mathbf{q} \wedge (\mathbf{p} \wedge \mathbf{r})] = (\mathbf{p} \cdot \mathbf{p})(\mathbf{q} \cdot \mathbf{r}) - (\mathbf{p} \cdot \mathbf{q})(\mathbf{p} \cdot \mathbf{r}),$$

31

which gives on taking moduli,

$$\sin c \sin b \cos A = \cos a - \cos b \cos c.$$

By symmetry, two similar formulae are obtained by cyclic permutation of a, b, c and A, B, C. $\square$

2.5 The Solution of Vector Equations

Problem 2.18 Solve the vector equation for **x**:

$$\mathbf{x} \wedge \mathbf{a} = \mathbf{b}, \qquad (2.22)$$

where **a** and **b** are given vectors.

Solution. If we form the scalar product on each side with **a** we get

$$0 = \mathbf{a} . \mathbf{b},$$

which shows that (2.22) cannot hold unless this condition on **a** and **b** is satisfied. Suppose that $\mathbf{a} . \mathbf{b} = 0$. Form the vector product of **a** and (2.22):

$$\mathbf{a} \wedge (\mathbf{x} \wedge \mathbf{a}) = a^2 \mathbf{x} - (\mathbf{a} . \mathbf{x})\mathbf{a} = \mathbf{a} \wedge \mathbf{b},$$

and therefore if $\mathbf{a} \neq 0$ we can write

$$\mathbf{x} = \frac{\mathbf{a} \wedge \mathbf{b}}{a^2} + \frac{\mathbf{a} . \mathbf{x}}{a^2} \mathbf{a}. \qquad (2.23)$$

(When $\mathbf{a} = 0$ it follows from (2.22) that $\mathbf{b} = 0$ and **x** is arbitrary; otherwise there is no solution.)

Equation (2.23) does not constitute a solution of (2.22) since the unknown appears on both sides, but it demonstrates that any solution must consist of the sum of the known vector $(\mathbf{a} \wedge \mathbf{b})/a^2$ and a certain vector parallel to **a**, for the right-hand side of (2.23) is of this form whatever the value of **x**. Thus, the solution is of the form

$$\mathbf{x} = \frac{\mathbf{a} \wedge \mathbf{b}}{a^2} + \lambda \mathbf{a}, \qquad (2.24)$$

where the scalar λ is to be determined.

Having reduced the problem to the determination of an unknown scalar rather than an unknown vector, solving is much simplified. Substitute (2.24) in (2.22). The left-hand side becomes

$$\frac{(\mathbf{a} \wedge \mathbf{b}) \wedge \mathbf{a}}{a^2} + \lambda \mathbf{a} \wedge \mathbf{a} = \frac{a^2 \mathbf{b} - (\mathbf{a} . \mathbf{b})\mathbf{a}}{a^2} = \mathbf{b},$$

since $\mathbf{a} . \mathbf{b} = 0$, $\mathbf{a} \wedge \mathbf{a} = 0$. Thus, (2.22) is satisfied whatever the value of λ, and so (2.24) is the solution with λ an arbitrary scalar.

We can give a simple geometrical interpretation to (2.22). Provided that **a** is orthogonal to **b**, it is the equation of a straight line through the point $(\mathbf{a} \wedge \mathbf{b})/a^2$ parallel to the vector **a**. Since both terms on the right in (2.24) are orthogonal to **b**, **b** is normal to the plane of this straight line and the origin. □

The solution of vector equations usually involves 'multiplying' both sides by one of the known vectors to allow the expansion of a triple product containing the unknown vector (as in this example) or to eliminate some unknown terms.

Problem 2.19 Solve the vector equation for **x**:

$$k\mathbf{x}+(\mathbf{x}.\mathbf{a})\mathbf{b} = \mathbf{c}, \qquad (k \neq 0). \tag{2.25}$$

Solution: *Method* 1. The equation is solved once the unknown scalar **x**.**a** is determined, since **x** can then be obtained by rearrangement of (2.25). Form the scalar product with **a**. Then

$$k\mathbf{x}.\mathbf{a}+(\mathbf{x}.\mathbf{a})(\mathbf{b}.\mathbf{a}) = \mathbf{c}.\mathbf{a},$$

i.e. $$(k+\mathbf{b}.\mathbf{a})\mathbf{x}.\mathbf{a} = \mathbf{c}.\mathbf{a}. \tag{2.26}$$

There are two cases to consider:

(i) $k+\mathbf{b}.\mathbf{a} \neq 0$. Substitution for **x**.**a** from (2.26) in (2.25) gives

$$\mathbf{x} = \frac{1}{k}\left(\mathbf{c}-\frac{\mathbf{c}.\mathbf{a}}{k+\mathbf{b}.\mathbf{a}}\mathbf{b}\right). \tag{2.27}$$

This may indeed be verified as the solution of (2.25) by substitution in the left-hand side. It is advisable to check solutions of vector equations in this way because extraneous roots may have been introduced (especially in the course of forming scalar products).

(ii) $k+\mathbf{b}.\mathbf{a} = 0$. In this case, (2.26) shows that there can be no solution unless $\mathbf{c}.\mathbf{a} = 0$. If $\mathbf{c}.\mathbf{a} = 0$, then (2.26) does not determine a unique value for **x**.**a**. Write $\mathbf{x}.\mathbf{a} = \alpha$. By (2.25),

$$\mathbf{x} = k^{-1}(\mathbf{c}-\alpha\mathbf{b}). \tag{2.28}$$

Every solution of (2.25) must therefore have this form, and we can substitute back for **x** in both terms to find α. Details are left to the reader; it emerges that a solution is obtained for arbitrary α.

Method 2. We can proceed along the lines of (ii) for all cases. Substitute (2.28) in (2.25). After a little reduction, we find that the latter is satisfied provided that

$$[\mathbf{c}.\mathbf{a}-\alpha(k+\mathbf{b}.\mathbf{a})]\mathbf{b} = 0.$$

We assume that $\mathbf{b} \neq 0$; otherwise (2.25) is trivial. Two cases have to be considered, as before. If $k+\mathbf{b}.\mathbf{a} \neq 0$, then

$$\alpha = \frac{\mathbf{c}.\mathbf{a}}{k+\mathbf{b}.\mathbf{a}}.$$

If $k+\mathbf{b}.\mathbf{a} = 0$, then α is arbitrary provided $\mathbf{c}.\mathbf{a} = 0$, and there is no solution otherwise.

For these values of α, (2.28) provides the solution to the given vector equation, in agreement with that previously obtained. One advantage in Method 2 is that no further checking is necessary, as checking is carried out in the course of the working. □

Problem 2.20 Solve the vector equation for $\mathbf{x}$:

$$\mathbf{x} \wedge \mathbf{a} + (\mathbf{x}.\mathbf{b})\mathbf{a} = \mathbf{c}. \tag{2.29}$$

Solution. Form the vector product with $\mathbf{a}$ to permit expansion of the first term on the left and to eliminate the second term. Thus

$$\mathbf{a} \wedge (\mathbf{x} \wedge \mathbf{a}) = a^2\mathbf{x} - (\mathbf{a}.\mathbf{x})\mathbf{a} = \mathbf{a} \wedge \mathbf{c},$$

so that any solution of (2.29) must be expressible in the form

$$\mathbf{x} = \frac{\mathbf{a} \wedge \mathbf{c}}{a^2} + \lambda\mathbf{a}, \tag{2.30}$$

for some value of the scalar λ, where we have written λ to denote $(\mathbf{a}.\mathbf{x})/a^2$. Substitution of (2.30) in (2.29) gives, after some reduction,

$$\mathbf{c} - \frac{\mathbf{a}.\mathbf{c}}{a^2}\mathbf{a} + \frac{(\mathbf{a} \wedge \mathbf{c}).\mathbf{b}}{a^2}\mathbf{a} + \lambda(\mathbf{a}.\mathbf{b})\mathbf{a} = \mathbf{c}$$

whence, except in the trivial case $\mathbf{a} = 0$, we get

$$(\mathbf{a}.\mathbf{b})\lambda = \frac{\mathbf{a}.(\mathbf{c} - \mathbf{c} \wedge \mathbf{b})}{a^2}. \tag{2.31}$$

If $\mathbf{a}.\mathbf{b} \neq 0$, this equation determines a unique value of λ, and we get

$$\mathbf{x} = \frac{1}{a^2}\left[\mathbf{a} \wedge \mathbf{c} + \frac{\mathbf{a}.(\mathbf{c} - \mathbf{c} \wedge \mathbf{b})}{\mathbf{a}.\mathbf{b}}\mathbf{a}\right].$$

If $\mathbf{a}.\mathbf{b} = 0$, then (2.31) can be satisfied only when the right-hand side is zero, in which case λ is arbitrary. Hence, if $\mathbf{a}.(\mathbf{c} - \mathbf{c} \wedge \mathbf{b}) \neq 0$, there is no solution, and if $\mathbf{a}.(\mathbf{c} - \mathbf{c} \wedge \mathbf{b}) = 0$ the solution of (2.29) is given by (2.30) with λ arbitrary. □

Problem 2.21 Solve the simultaneous vector equations for $\mathbf{x}$ and $\mathbf{y}$:

$$\mathbf{x} + \mathbf{c} \wedge \mathbf{y} = \mathbf{a},$$
$$\mathbf{y} + \mathbf{c} \wedge \mathbf{x} = \mathbf{b}.$$

Solution. Substitute for $\mathbf{y}$ from the second equation into the first. Thus,

$$\mathbf{x} + \mathbf{c} \wedge (\mathbf{b} - \mathbf{c} \wedge \mathbf{x}) = \mathbf{a},$$

or, on expanding the triple product,

$$(1 + c^2)\mathbf{x} = \lambda\mathbf{c} + \mathbf{a} + \mathbf{b} \wedge \mathbf{c}, \tag{2.32}$$

where λ denotes $\mathbf{x} \cdot \mathbf{c}$. By symmetry, we must likewise have

$$(1+c^2)\mathbf{y} = \mu\mathbf{c}+\mathbf{b}+\mathbf{a}\wedge\mathbf{c}, \tag{2.33}$$

where $\mu = \mathbf{y} \cdot \mathbf{c}$.

Next, determine λ and μ by substituting for $\mathbf{x}$ and $\mathbf{y}$ from (2.32), (2.33) into the given equations. The latter are found to reduce to

$$(\lambda-\mathbf{a}\cdot\mathbf{c})\mathbf{c} = 0,$$
$$(\mu-\mathbf{b}\cdot\mathbf{c})\mathbf{c} = 0,$$

whence, except in the trivial case $\mathbf{c} = 0$, we obtain

$$\lambda = \mathbf{a}\cdot\mathbf{c}, \qquad \mu = \mathbf{b}\cdot\mathbf{c}.$$

Therefore, by (2.32), (2.33) we obtain for the required solution

$$\mathbf{x} = [(\mathbf{a}\cdot\mathbf{c})\mathbf{c}+\mathbf{a}+\mathbf{b}\wedge\mathbf{c}]/(1+c^2),$$
$$\mathbf{y} = [(\mathbf{b}\cdot\mathbf{c})\mathbf{c}+\mathbf{b}+\mathbf{a}\wedge\mathbf{c}]/(1+c^2). \qquad \square$$

EXERCISES

1. Show that the line $\mathbf{r} = \mathbf{i}+\mathbf{j}-2\mathbf{k}+\lambda(\mathbf{j}+\mathbf{k})$ and the points $(2, 3, 3)$, $(2, -1, -1)$ lie in a plane.

2. Find the set of vectors reciprocal to the set $\mathbf{i}+\mathbf{j}, \mathbf{j}+\mathbf{k}, \mathbf{k}+\mathbf{i}$.

3. Express the vector equation of the plane in Problem 1.27 in the scalar product form $\mathbf{r}\cdot\mathbf{n} = q$.

4. A force of magnitude 6 units acts along the line $\mathbf{r} = \mathbf{i}+\mathbf{k}+t(\mathbf{j}-\mathbf{k})$ in the direction t increasing. Find its vector moment about the point $P(2, 1, -1)$, and also its scalar moment about an axis, passing through P, having the direction of $\mathbf{i}+2\mathbf{j}+2\mathbf{k}$.

5. Find the point of intersection of the planes $\mathbf{r}\cdot\mathbf{a} = \alpha, \mathbf{r}\cdot\mathbf{b} = \beta, \mathbf{r}\cdot\mathbf{c} = \gamma$, where $\mathbf{a}, \mathbf{b}, \mathbf{c}$ are given non-coplanar vectors and α, β, γ are given scalars. (Hint: resolve $\mathbf{r}$ in the directions of the reciprocal vectors to $\mathbf{a}, \mathbf{b}, \mathbf{c}$.)

6. Prove the identity

$$(\mathbf{a}\wedge\mathbf{b})\cdot[(\mathbf{c}\wedge\mathbf{d})\wedge(\mathbf{e}\wedge\mathbf{f})] = [(\mathbf{a}\wedge\mathbf{c})\cdot\mathbf{d}][(\mathbf{b}\wedge\mathbf{e})\cdot\mathbf{f}]-[(\mathbf{b}\wedge\mathbf{c})\cdot\mathbf{d}][(\mathbf{a}\wedge\mathbf{e})\cdot\mathbf{f}].$$

7. Solve the simultaneous vector equations for $\mathbf{x}$ and $\mathbf{y}$:

$$\mathbf{x}+\mathbf{y} = \mathbf{a}, \quad \mathbf{x}\wedge\mathbf{y} = \mathbf{b},$$

where $\mathbf{a}$ and $\mathbf{b}$ are given mutually orthogonal vectors.

8. Solve the simultaneous vector equations:

$$2\mathbf{x}+\mathbf{y}\wedge\mathbf{a} = \mathbf{b}, \quad 3\mathbf{y}+\mathbf{x}\wedge\mathbf{a} = \mathbf{c},$$

where $\mathbf{a}, \mathbf{b}, \mathbf{c}$ are given vectors.

Chapter 3

Equivalent Systems of Forces

3.1 Equivalence The position and orientation of a rigid body in space is specified by six independent coordinates. For example, if ABC is a triangle fixed in the body, then three coordinates are necessary to locate A, two more are needed to determine the direction of AB, and a sixth determines the angular position of C about the axis AB. The coordinates may be chosen in various ways, but the number is always the same and we say that a rigid body has six *degrees of freedom* in three-dimensional space.

A consequence is that the mechanical effect of a system of forces acting at various points in a rigid body is determined entirely by two vector (six scalar) quantities. In particular, these can be taken to be the vector resultant and the vector sum of the moments of the forces about the origin. Thus, a system of forces $\mathbf{F}_i$ ($i = 1, 2, \ldots, n$) acting at points with position vectors $\mathbf{r}_i$ has the same mechanical effect on the body as a second system $\mathbf{F}'_j$ ($j = 1, 2, \ldots, m$) acting at points $\mathbf{r}'_j$ if

$$\sum_{i=1}^{n} \mathbf{F}_i = \sum_{j=1}^{m} \mathbf{F}'_j, \tag{3.1}$$

$$\sum_{i=1}^{n} \mathbf{r}_i \wedge \mathbf{F}_i = \sum_{j=1}^{m} \mathbf{r}'_j \wedge \mathbf{F}'_j. \tag{3.2}$$

If these conditions hold, then the two systems of forces are said to be *equivalent*.

Problem 3.1 A system consisting of two equal and opposite forces $\mathbf{F}, -\mathbf{F}$ whose lines of action are not coincident is known as a *couple*. If the lines of action pass through the points A, B, respectively, then the vector $\mathbf{BA} \wedge \mathbf{F}$ is the *moment of the couple* (Fig. 3.1). Prove that the moment

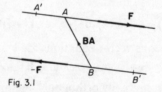

Fig. 3.1

is independent of the positions of the points A and B on the lines of action. Prove also that two couples with the same moment are equivalent systems of forces.

Solution. Let A, A' be distinct points on the line of action of $\mathbf{F}$, and

36

let B, B' be distinct points on the line of action of $-\mathbf{F}$. We shall show that $\mathbf{B'A'} \wedge \mathbf{F} = \mathbf{BA} \wedge \mathbf{F}$, so that the moment of the couple is the same whether we choose A and B or A' and B' as the two points. We have simply,

$$\mathbf{BA} \wedge \mathbf{F} = (\mathbf{BB'} + \mathbf{B'A'} + \mathbf{A'A}) \wedge \mathbf{F} = \mathbf{B'A'} \wedge \mathbf{F},$$

since $\mathbf{BB'}$ and $\mathbf{A'A}$ are both parallel to $\mathbf{F}$.

The vector resultant of the forces forming a couple is zero, since $\mathbf{F} + (-\mathbf{F}) = 0$. Therefore (3.1) is satisfied whenever the two sides refer to couples.

The vector sum of the moments about O of the forces $\mathbf{F}, -\mathbf{F}$ is

$$\mathbf{OA} \wedge \mathbf{F} + \mathbf{OB} \wedge (-\mathbf{F}) = (\mathbf{OA} - \mathbf{OB}) \wedge \mathbf{F}$$
$$= \mathbf{BA} \wedge \mathbf{F} = \mathbf{G},$$

where $\mathbf{G}$ is the moment of the couple. It follows that for systems comprising couples with the same moment $\mathbf{G}$, each side of (3.2) is equal to $\mathbf{G}$. Hence two couples with the same moment are equivalent systems. ☐

Problem 3.2 Prove that any system of couples with moments $\mathbf{G}_1$, $\mathbf{G}_2, \ldots, \mathbf{G}_r$ is equivalent to one couple with moment $\sum_{i=1}^{r} \mathbf{G}_i$.

Solution. The vector resultant of the forces forming any one couple $\mathbf{G}_i$ is zero, and hence the vector resultant of the $2r$ forces in all the r couples is zero.

The vector sum of the moments about O of the $2r$ forces comprising the given couples is, by addition, $\sum \mathbf{G}_i$. Therefore the system is equivalent to one couple with moment $\sum \mathbf{G}_i$, since these two systems have the same (zero) vector resultant and the same vector sum of moments about the origin. ☐

3.2 Parallel Forces

Problem 3.3 Show that any pair of parallel forces is equivalent to a single force, unless they form a couple.

Solution. Let the forces be $\mathbf{F}$ and $k\mathbf{F}$, and let $\mathbf{r}_1$ and $\mathbf{r}_2$ be points on the respective lines of action. We may suppose that the lines of action are not coincident; for otherwise the result is immediate, the system being equivalent to a force $(k+1)\mathbf{F}$ (which is zero in the case $k = -1$) with the same line of action.

A single force $(k+1)\mathbf{F}$ is equivalent to the two parallel forces if its line of action passes through a point $\mathbf{r}_3$, such that

$$\mathbf{r}_3 \wedge (k+1)\mathbf{F} = \mathbf{r}_1 \wedge \mathbf{F} + \mathbf{r}_2 \wedge k\mathbf{F}, \tag{3.3}$$

since it will have the same resultant and same vector sum of moments about O. Provided that $k \neq -1$, (3.3) can be satisfied by taking

$$\mathbf{r}_3 = \frac{\mathbf{r}_1 + k\mathbf{r}_2}{k+1},$$

(which we recognise as the position vector of the point dividing the line segment joining the points $\mathbf{r}_1$ and $\mathbf{r}_2$ in the ratio $k:1$). The point $\mathbf{r}_3$ is not uniquely determined by (3.3), though the line of action of the single force $(k+1)\mathbf{F}$ is determined. (The proof consists in interpreting (3.3) as the equation of a straight line; *c.f.* (2.22) and remarks in Problem 2.18.)

When $k = -1$, the two given forces form a couple. There is no solution to (3.3) in this case unless the right-hand side (the moment of the couple) is zero, i.e. the lines of action are coincident. ☐

Problem 3.4 Parallel forces $p(\mathbf{i}+\mathbf{j})$, $q(\mathbf{i}+\mathbf{j})$, $(1-p-q)(\mathbf{i}+\mathbf{j})$ act through the points with position vectors $\mathbf{j}$, $\mathbf{k}$, $-(2\mathbf{i}+\mathbf{j}+\mathbf{k})$, respectively, where p and q are given real numbers. Show that they are equivalent to a single force. Find the equation of its line of action, and show that this passes through the origin if, and only if, $p = -1$, $q = 1$.

Solution. We show more generally that any three parallel forces are equivalent to a single force (which may be zero) or a couple. For, there will be at least two with the same sense of direction, which cannot together form a couple. By Problem 3.3, these two forces are equivalent to a single force. If we combine this with the third given force, we obtain a parallel pair equivalent to the original system. But, by Problem 3.3, the parallel pair is equivalent to a single force or a couple, whence the result follows. (A generalization to any number of parallel forces is evident.)

For the system in question, the resultant is $\mathbf{R} = \mathbf{i}+\mathbf{j} \neq 0$, which proves that the system is not equivalent to a couple. Let $\mathbf{r}$ be the position vector on the line of action of the single equivalent force. Then, equating vector moments about O, we have

$$\mathbf{r} \wedge (\mathbf{i}+\mathbf{j}) = \mathbf{j} \wedge p(\mathbf{i}+\mathbf{j}) + \mathbf{k} \wedge q(\mathbf{i}+\mathbf{j}) - (2\mathbf{i}+\mathbf{j}+\mathbf{k}) \wedge (1-p-q)(\mathbf{i}+\mathbf{j})$$

$$= -p\mathbf{k} + q(\mathbf{j}-\mathbf{i}) - (1-p-q)(-\mathbf{i}+\mathbf{j}+\mathbf{k})$$

$$= (1-p-2q)\mathbf{i} + (p+2q-1)\mathbf{j} + (q-1)\mathbf{k}. \qquad (3.4)$$

This is the equation of the line of action in the form (2.22) (*c.f.* Problem 2.18.)

The line of action passes through the origin if (3.4) is satisfied when we put $\mathbf{r} = 0$. The condition for this is that the coefficients of $\mathbf{i}$, $\mathbf{j}$ and $\mathbf{k}$ on the right all vanish:

$$1-p-2q = 0, \quad p+2q-1 = 0, \quad q-1 = 0.$$

Solving these simultaneous linear equations, we find the required condition $p = -1, q = 1$. $\square$

3.3 Systems in General

Every system of forces $\mathbf{F}_i$ acting at points $\mathbf{r}_i$ is equivalent to a single force $\mathbf{R} = \sum \mathbf{F}_i$ acting through the origin O, together with a couple of moment $\mathbf{G} = \sum \mathbf{r}_i \wedge \mathbf{F}_i$. This is evident from (3.1), (3.2). If a different point O' is taken as origin, the couple is in general changed because the sum of the moments of the forces is not the same about every origin, although the single force $\mathbf{R}$ does not change.

The effect of changing the origin from O to O' can be understood by introducing mutually cancelling forces $\mathbf{R}, -\mathbf{R}$ at O'. The forces $\mathbf{R}$ at O and $-\mathbf{R}$ at O' form a couple of moment $\mathbf{O'O} \wedge \mathbf{R}$, and so the original system is equivalent to a force $\mathbf{R}$ through O' together with a couple of moment $\mathbf{G'} = \mathbf{G} - \mathbf{a} \wedge \mathbf{R}$, where $\mathbf{a} = \mathbf{OO'}$.

Since

$$\mathbf{R} \cdot \mathbf{G'} = \mathbf{R} \cdot (\mathbf{G} - \mathbf{a} \wedge \mathbf{R}) = \mathbf{R} \cdot \mathbf{G}, \qquad (3.5)$$

there are two scalar *invariants* for the system, namely, R^2 and $\mathbf{R} \cdot \mathbf{G}$. These can be evaluated using any point as origin, and can be used to distinguish possible cases. If a system of forces is equivalent to a couple only, or to zero (equilibrium), then both invariants are zero. If the system is equivalent to a single force, then $R^2 \neq 0$, $\mathbf{R} \cdot \mathbf{G} = 0$. (Take any point on the line of action as origin. Then $\mathbf{G} = 0$, so that $\mathbf{R} \cdot \mathbf{G} = 0$.) If it is equivalent to a force and a couple, neither invariant vanishes.

Problem 3.5 A set of forces act along the edges of a tetrahedron $OABC$, being given in magnitude, direction and line of action by the vectors $l\mathbf{OA}$, $m\mathbf{OB}$, $n\mathbf{OC}$, $p\mathbf{BC}$, $q\mathbf{CA}$, $r\mathbf{AB}$, where l, m, n, p, q, r are real numbers with $l + m + n > 0$. Prove that the condition for the set to be equivalent to a single force is that $lp + mq + nr = 0$.

Solution. Take O as origin. The vectors along the edges are not independent; we can write $\mathbf{AB} = \mathbf{OB} - \mathbf{OA}$, $\mathbf{BC} = \mathbf{OC} - \mathbf{OB}$, $\mathbf{CA} = \mathbf{OA} - \mathbf{OC}$. Then by forming the vector sum of all the forces we find

$$\mathbf{R} = (l + q - r)\mathbf{OA} + (m + r - p)\mathbf{OB} + (n + p - q)\mathbf{OC}. \qquad (3.6)$$

Since the three vectors on the right are in non-coplanar directions, $\mathbf{R} = 0$ only if the three bracketed expressions all vanish. But their sum is $l + m + n$, which is given to be non-zero. Hence we have $\mathbf{R} \neq 0$, and $R^2 \neq 0$.

The three forces whose lines of action pass through O have zero moment about O. The moment of the force $p\mathbf{BC}$ about O is

$$\mathbf{OB} \wedge p\mathbf{BC} = p\mathbf{OB} \wedge (\mathbf{OC} - \mathbf{OB}) = p\mathbf{OB} \wedge \mathbf{OC}.$$

39

Treating the remaining forces similarly we find for the sum of the moments about O

$$\mathbf{G} = p\mathbf{OB} \wedge \mathbf{OC} + q\mathbf{OC} \wedge \mathbf{OA} + r\mathbf{OA} \wedge \mathbf{OB},$$

whence by (3.6) we find

$$\mathbf{R} \cdot \mathbf{G} = [p(l+q-r)+q(m+r-p)+r(n+p-q)]V,$$

where $V = \mathbf{OA} \cdot (\mathbf{OB} \wedge \mathbf{OC}) \neq 0$ since $|V|$ is the volume of the tetrahedron. It follows that $\mathbf{R} \cdot \mathbf{G}$ vanishes only when the expression in square brackets vanishes, and this simplifies to the condition $lp + mq + nr = 0$. In this case, the system of forces is equivalent to a single force. $\square$

***Problem* 3.6** (*Central axis*)   Let a system of forces be equivalent to $(\mathbf{R}, \mathbf{G})$ when O is the origin. To find the locus of a point O' such that $\mathbf{G}'$, in the notation of equation (3.5), is parallel to $\mathbf{R}$.

Solution. We require $\mathbf{G}' \wedge \mathbf{R} = 0$, i.e.

$$(\mathbf{G} - \mathbf{r} \wedge \mathbf{R}) \wedge \mathbf{R} = 0$$

where $\mathbf{r} = \mathbf{OO}'$. On expanding the triple product and rearranging we obtain (*cf.* Problem 2.19)

$$\mathbf{r} = \mathbf{R} \wedge \mathbf{G}/R^2 + t\mathbf{R}, \tag{3.7}$$

where t denotes $\mathbf{r} \cdot \mathbf{R}$. Thus, every point on the required locus lies on the straight line which passes through the point $\mathbf{R} \wedge \mathbf{G}/R^2$ and is parallel to $\mathbf{R}$. This line exists provided only that $\mathbf{R} \neq 0$.

We easily find by substituting (3.7) into the previous equation that the entire line is the locus; i.e. t is arbitrary. The locus is known as the *central axis* of the system, and the equivalent force and couple $(\mathbf{R}, \mathbf{G}')$ comprise a thrust along the central axis and a torque about the axis. A couple, and a force parallel to the moment of the couple, together form a *wrench*.

Let $\mathbf{G}' = p\mathbf{R}$. Then $p = \mathbf{R} \cdot \mathbf{G}'/R^2 = \mathbf{R} \cdot \mathbf{G}/R^2$ is the *pitch* of the wrench, and measures the ratio of the torque about the central axis to the thrust along it. When p is positive (negative) the torque is in the direction of a positive (negative) rotation with respect to $\mathbf{R}$. $\square$

***Problem* 3.7**   A system consists of forces $\mathbf{F}_1 = 3\mathbf{i} + 2\mathbf{k}$, $\mathbf{F}_2 = \mathbf{j} - 2\mathbf{k}$, $\mathbf{F}_3 = \mathbf{i} + \mathbf{j} + \mathbf{k}$ acting at points $\mathbf{r}_1 = \mathbf{i}$, $\mathbf{r}_2 = \mathbf{i} - 2\mathbf{j}$, $\mathbf{r}_3 = 2\mathbf{j} - \mathbf{k}$, respectively. Find the equation of the central axis, and the pitch of the equivalent wrench.

Solution. We have

$$\mathbf{R} = \mathbf{F}_1 + \mathbf{F}_2 + \mathbf{F}_3 = 4\mathbf{i} + 2\mathbf{j} + \mathbf{k}.$$

Also,

$$\begin{aligned}
\mathbf{G} &= \mathbf{r}_1 \wedge \mathbf{F}_1 + \mathbf{r}_2 \wedge \mathbf{F}_2 + \mathbf{r}_3 \wedge \mathbf{F}_3 \\
&= -2\mathbf{j} + (4\mathbf{i} + 2\mathbf{j} + \mathbf{k}) + (3\mathbf{i} - \mathbf{j} - 2\mathbf{k}) \\
&= 7\mathbf{i} - \mathbf{j} - \mathbf{k}.
\end{aligned}$$

Thus, $R^2 = 21$, $\mathbf{R}\cdot\mathbf{G} = 25$, $\mathbf{R}\wedge\mathbf{G} = -\mathbf{i}+11\mathbf{j}-18\mathbf{k}$.

The equation of the central axis is

$$\mathbf{r} = \tfrac{1}{21}(-\mathbf{i}+11\mathbf{j}-18\mathbf{k})+t(4\mathbf{i}+2\mathbf{j}+\mathbf{k}), \qquad (3.8)$$

and the pitch of the equivalent wrench is

$$p = \mathbf{R}\cdot\mathbf{G}/R^2 = 25/21.$$

Because p is positive, the torque of the couple corresponds to a positive rotation with respect to $\mathbf{R}$.

Note that $\mathbf{G}'$ is the same for every point O' on the central axis, because $\mathbf{G}' = p\mathbf{R}$, where p is a constant for the system. In the above example, $\mathbf{G}' = (25/21)(4\mathbf{i}+2\mathbf{j}+\mathbf{k})$ for each such point O'. □

Problem 3.8 Find the equation of the *null plane* at the point $\mathbf{i}+\mathbf{j}$ for the system in Problem 3.7.

Solution. Consider a system which is equivalent to a force $\mathbf{R}$ acting through A, together with a couple $\mathbf{G}'$. If $\mathbf{OA} = \mathbf{a}$, then

$$\mathbf{G}' = \mathbf{G}-\mathbf{a}\wedge\mathbf{R}.$$

Since the total vector moment of all the forces about A is $\mathbf{G}'$, the total scalar moment about any axis through A lying in the plane perpendicular to $\mathbf{G}'$ is zero. This plane is the *null plane* at A. Its equation is

$$(\mathbf{r}-\mathbf{a})\cdot(\mathbf{G}-\mathbf{a}\wedge\mathbf{R}) = 0,$$

or
$$\mathbf{r}\cdot(\mathbf{G}-\mathbf{a}\wedge\mathbf{R}) = \mathbf{a}\cdot\mathbf{G}. \qquad (3.9)$$

For the system in Problem 3.7 we find, when $\mathbf{a} = \mathbf{i}+\mathbf{j}$, that this is the plane

$$\mathbf{r}\cdot(6\mathbf{i}+\mathbf{k}) = 6,$$

i.e.
$$6x+z = 6.$$

EXERCISES

1. Find the resultant of parallel forces 6, -4, -3, 2, 2 in the direction of the vector $\mathbf{j}+\mathbf{k}$. If the respective lines of action pass through the points $(1,0,1)$, $(-1,2,0)$, $(2,1,3)$, $(-3,-1,2)$, $(0,1,2)$, find the vector sum of the moments about the origin, and obtain the equation of the line of action of the equivalent single force.

2. If $\mathbf{a}$ is the unit vector $\tfrac{1}{3}(2\mathbf{i}-2\mathbf{j}+\mathbf{k})$, find the real numbers p and q for which the forces $2\mathbf{a}$, $p\mathbf{a}$, $q\mathbf{a}$, $(1-p+q)\mathbf{a}$ acting at the points $\mathbf{i}+\mathbf{j}$, $\mathbf{i}-\mathbf{j}$, $\mathbf{i}+\mathbf{j}+\mathbf{k}$, $2\mathbf{i}-\mathbf{j}-\mathbf{k}$, respectively, are equivalent to (i) zero, (ii) a single force, (iii) a couple.

3. A system of forces of magnitudes 1, 3, 3 act along lines $\mathbf{i}+\lambda(\mathbf{i}+2\mathbf{j}+2\mathbf{k})$,

$\mathbf{j}+\mu(\mathbf{i}-2\mathbf{j}-2\mathbf{k})$, $\mathbf{k}+\nu(2\mathbf{i}-2\mathbf{j}+\mathbf{k})$ in the directions λ, μ, ν increasing, respectively. Find (i) the scalar invariants R^2 and $\mathbf{R}.\,\mathbf{G}$; (ii) the equation of the central axis of the system; (iii) the pitch of the equivalent wrench.

4. In the notation of (3.5), show that the couple $\mathbf{G'}$ has least magnitude when O' is a point on the central axis of the system.

5. Find the normal to the null plane at the point $(1,0,0)$ for the system of forces in Exercise 3.

6. The sum of the moments of a given system of forces about a general point O' is $\mathbf{G'}$. Let A' be the point such that $\mathbf{O'A'} = \mathbf{G'}$. Show that if O' moves along any straight line, then the locus of A' is also a straight line.

Chapter 4

Differentiation and Integration of Vectors

4.1 Differentiation with Respect to One Scalar Variable The position vector of a moving particle depends on the time, t and is said to be a *vector function* of the scalar t. Alternatively, it can be considered to be a function of the distance, s, travelled along the path, measured from a convenient point. At each instant of the motion we can construct the unit tangent vector to the path, pointing in the direction of motion, and this, too, is a vector function of t or of s. These are examples of vector functions of one scalar variable.

Let $\mathbf{a}$ be a (vector) function of the scalar variable u; write $\mathbf{a} = \mathbf{a}(u)$. The change in $\mathbf{a}$ as u undergoes a small increment from $u = u_0$ to $u = u_0 + \Delta u$ is

$$\Delta \mathbf{a} = \mathbf{a}(u_0 + \Delta u) - \mathbf{a}(u_0).$$

If $|\Delta \mathbf{a}| \to 0$ as $\Delta u \to 0$, then $\mathbf{a}(u)$ is said to be a *continuous* function of u at $u = u_0$. If, additionally, the ratio $\Delta \mathbf{a}/\Delta u$ tends to a finite limit as Δu tends to zero, the limit is called the *derivative* of $\mathbf{a}$ with respect to u, at u_0, and is written $d\mathbf{a}/du$. When it exists, the derivative is itself a vector.

Problem 4.1 The position vector $\mathbf{r}$ of a moving particle at time t is given by the equation $\mathbf{r} = \mathbf{b} + t\mathbf{c}$, where $\mathbf{b}$ and $\mathbf{c}$ are constant vectors. Find the *velocity* and *acceleration vectors* at time t.

Solution. The *velocity vector* is here defined to be the derivative of the position vector (relative to a fixed origin) with respect to time. We shall see in the next problem that if non-zero, this is in all cases tangential to the path, pointing in the forward direction of motion, and having magnitude equal to the speed. The *acceleration vector* is the derivative, with respect to time, of the velocity vector.

In the present case, the motion takes place along the straight line through the point $\mathbf{b}$ in the direction $\mathbf{c}$ (Fig. 4.1). If P and P' denote the points occupied by the particle at times t, $t + \Delta t$, respectively, then

$$\Delta \mathbf{r} = \mathbf{PP'} = \mathbf{r}(t + \Delta t) - \mathbf{r}(t)$$
$$= \mathbf{b} + (t + \Delta t)\mathbf{c} - (\mathbf{b} + t\mathbf{c})$$
$$= \Delta t\, \mathbf{c},$$

and so the velocity vector is

$$\mathbf{v} = \frac{d\mathbf{r}}{dt} = \lim_{\Delta t \to 0} \frac{\Delta \mathbf{r}}{\Delta t} = \mathbf{c},$$

43

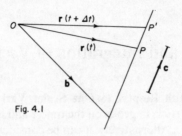

Fig. 4.1

which is constant. The acceleration vector is

$$\mathbf{a} = \frac{d\mathbf{v}}{dt} = \lim_{\Delta t \to 0} \frac{\Delta \mathbf{v}}{\Delta t},$$

where

$$\Delta \mathbf{v} = \mathbf{v}(t + \Delta t) - \mathbf{v}(t) = \mathbf{c} - \mathbf{c} = 0.$$

Hence the acceleration vector is zero. □

Problem 4.2 Show that the velocity vector of a moving particle has magnitude equal to the speed, and direction tangential to the path in the forward direction of motion.

Solution. Let $\mathbf{r}(t)$ be the position vector of the particle at time t. If P and P' are the points occupied by the particle at times t, $t + \Delta t$, respectively, where $\Delta t > 0$, then the velocity vector $\mathbf{v} = \lim_{\Delta t \to 0} (\Delta \mathbf{r}/\Delta t)$, where

$$\frac{\Delta \mathbf{r}}{\Delta t} = \frac{\mathbf{r}(t + \Delta t) - \mathbf{r}(t)}{\Delta t} = \frac{1}{\Delta t} \mathbf{PP'}.$$

As Δt approaches 0, the point P' approaches P, and the limiting direction of $\mathbf{PP'}$ is tangential to the path, in the forward direction. This is the direction of $\mathbf{v}$.

The magnitude of $\mathbf{v}$ is the limit as $\Delta t \to 0$ of the ratio $|\mathbf{PP'}|/\Delta t$, which is equal to the speed at the point P. □

Problem 4.3 If $\mathbf{a}(u)$ denotes the vector $A(\cos u\, \mathbf{i} + \sin u\, \mathbf{j})$, where A is a positive constant, prove from first principles that

$$\frac{d^2 \mathbf{a}}{du^2} = -\mathbf{a}.$$

Solution. The notation $d^2\mathbf{a}/du^2$ denotes the second derivative of $\mathbf{a}$ with respect to u, i.e. $(d/du)(d\mathbf{a}/du)$.

Note that the magnitude of $\mathbf{a}$ is A. Since $\mathbf{a}$ has no z component, it can be considered as the position vector of a variable point P on the circle of radius A, centred at the origin, in the xy plane. (Fig. 4.2). If P corresponds to the value u, and P' to the value $u + \Delta u$, then xOP is the angle u and xOP' the angle $u + \Delta u$ (to within a multiple of 2π). We have

44

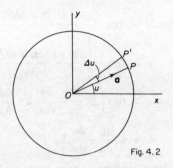

Fig. 4.2

$$\Delta \mathbf{a} = \mathbf{a}(u + \Delta u) - \mathbf{a}(u)$$
$$= A[\cos(u + \Delta u)\mathbf{i} + \sin(u + \Delta u)\mathbf{j}] - A(\cos u\,\mathbf{i} + \sin u\,\mathbf{j})$$
$$= A[\cos(u + \Delta u) - \cos u]\mathbf{i} + A[\sin(u + \Delta u) - \sin u]\mathbf{j}.$$

On dividing by Δu, and taking the limit as u tends to zero, we obtain for the coefficients of $\mathbf{i}$ and $\mathbf{j}$ respectively

$$A\frac{d}{du}\cos u = -A\sin u, \qquad A\frac{d}{du}\sin u = A\cos u,$$

so that
$$\frac{d\mathbf{a}}{du} = -A\sin u\,\mathbf{i} + A\cos u\,\mathbf{j}.$$

Proceeding in exactly the same way with this vector, we easily find that

$$\frac{d^2\mathbf{a}}{du^2} = -A\cos u\,\mathbf{i} - A\sin u\,\mathbf{j} = -\mathbf{a}.$$

This problem illustrates the general result that if $\mathbf{a}(u) = a_1(u)\mathbf{i} + a_2(u)\mathbf{j} + a_3(u)\mathbf{k}$, where a_1, a_2, a_3 possess derivatives with respect to u, then

$$\frac{d\mathbf{a}}{du} = \frac{da_1}{du}\mathbf{i} + \frac{da_2}{du}\mathbf{j} + \frac{da_3}{du}\mathbf{k}.$$

In particular, the rectangular components of the velocity vector $d\mathbf{r}/dt$ are $dx/dt, dy/dt, dz/dt$, where $\mathbf{r} = x\mathbf{i} + y\mathbf{j} + z\mathbf{k}$ relative to fixed axes. $\quad\square$

Problem 4.4 Prove that if $\mathbf{a} = \mathbf{a}(u)$, $\mathbf{b} = \mathbf{b}(u)$ have derivatives with respect to u, then

$$\frac{d}{du}(\mathbf{a}\cdot\mathbf{b}) = \mathbf{a}\cdot\frac{d\mathbf{b}}{du} + \frac{d\mathbf{a}}{du}\cdot\mathbf{b}.$$

Solution. We have

$$\Delta(\mathbf{a}\cdot\mathbf{b}) = (\mathbf{a} + \Delta\mathbf{a})\cdot(\mathbf{b} + \Delta\mathbf{b}) - \mathbf{a}\cdot\mathbf{b}.$$

45

Thus

$$\frac{d}{du}(\mathbf{a}.\mathbf{b}) = \lim_{\Delta u \to 0} \frac{(\mathbf{a}+\Delta\mathbf{a}).(\mathbf{b}+\Delta\mathbf{b})-\mathbf{a}.\mathbf{b}}{\Delta u}$$

$$= \lim \frac{\mathbf{a}.(\Delta\mathbf{b})+(\Delta\mathbf{a}).\mathbf{b}+(\Delta\mathbf{a}).(\Delta\mathbf{b})}{\Delta u}$$

$$= \lim \left(\mathbf{a}.\frac{\Delta\mathbf{b}}{\Delta u}+\frac{\Delta\mathbf{a}}{\Delta u}.\mathbf{b}+\frac{\Delta\mathbf{a}}{\Delta u}.\Delta\mathbf{b}\right)$$

$$= \mathbf{a}.\frac{d\mathbf{b}}{du}+\frac{d\mathbf{a}}{du}.\mathbf{b},$$

the third bracketed term tending to zero because $\Delta\mathbf{b}$ tends to zero.   □

In a similar way, the reader may verify the remainder of the following formulae which are numbered for reference:

(i) $\dfrac{d\mathbf{c}}{du} = 0, \quad$ if $\mathbf{c} = $ constant,

(ii) $\dfrac{d}{du}(\mathbf{a}+\mathbf{b}) = \dfrac{d\mathbf{a}}{du}+\dfrac{d\mathbf{b}}{du},$

(iii) $\dfrac{d}{dv}\mathbf{a}(u) = \dfrac{du}{dv}\dfrac{d\mathbf{a}}{du}, \quad$ if $u = u(v),$

(iv) $\dfrac{d}{du}(p\mathbf{a}) = p\dfrac{d\mathbf{a}}{du}+\dfrac{dp}{du}\mathbf{a},$

(v) $\dfrac{d}{du}(\mathbf{a}.\mathbf{b}) = \mathbf{a}.\dfrac{d\mathbf{b}}{du}+\dfrac{d\mathbf{a}}{du}.\mathbf{b},$

(vi) $\dfrac{d}{du}(\mathbf{a}\wedge\mathbf{b}) = \mathbf{a}\wedge\dfrac{d\mathbf{b}}{du}+\dfrac{d\mathbf{a}}{du}\wedge\mathbf{b},$

where p is a scalar and $\mathbf{a}$ and $\mathbf{b}$ are vector functions of u possessing the necessary derivatives. Care must be taken to keep $\mathbf{a}$ before $\mathbf{b}$ in the right-hand side of (vi).

Problem 4.5 Prove that if $\mathbf{r} = \mathbf{r}(t)$, then $\mathbf{r}.\dot{\mathbf{r}} = r\dot{r}$, where a dot denotes differentiation with respect to time. Interpret the result by using a diagram.

Solution. By formula (v),

$$\frac{d}{dt}(\mathbf{r}.\mathbf{r}) = \mathbf{r}.\dot{\mathbf{r}}+\dot{\mathbf{r}}.\mathbf{r} = 2\mathbf{r}.\dot{\mathbf{r}}.$$

But $\mathbf{r}.\mathbf{r} = r^2$, and $d(r^2)/dt = 2r\dot{r}$. Equating the right-hand sides of the two equations gives the required result.

Note that $\dot{\mathbf{r}} = (d/dt)\mathbf{r}$ is not to be confused with $\dot{r} = dr/dt$. In Fig. 4.3,

46

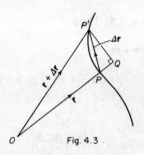

Fig. 4.3

$OP = r(t)$, $OP' = \mathbf{r} + \Delta \mathbf{r} = \mathbf{r}(t + \Delta t)$, and OQP' is a right-angle. Thus, $PP' = \Delta \mathbf{r}$, and so

$$PQ = \hat{\mathbf{r}} \cdot \Delta \mathbf{r}, \qquad OP \cdot PQ = r\hat{\mathbf{r}} \cdot \Delta \mathbf{r} = \mathbf{r} \cdot \Delta \mathbf{r}. \qquad (4.1)$$

To first order in small quantities,

$$PQ = OP' - OP = \Delta r, \qquad OP \cdot PQ = r \Delta r. \qquad (4.2)$$

The result follows from (4.1), (4.2) on dividing by Δt and proceeding to the limit as Δt tends to zero. $\qquad \square$

Problem 4.6 The velocity $\dot{\mathbf{r}}$ at a point P in a rigid body which rotates with constant angular velocity $\boldsymbol{\omega}$ about a fixed point O is given by $\dot{\mathbf{r}} = \boldsymbol{\omega} \wedge \mathbf{r}$, where $\mathbf{r} = OP$ and $\dot{\mathbf{r}} = d\mathbf{r}/dt$ (Problem 1.37). Determine the loci of points P for which (a) $\ddot{\mathbf{r}} = -\omega^2 \mathbf{r}$, (b) $d(\mathbf{r} \wedge \dot{\mathbf{r}})/dt = 0$.

Solution. (a)

$$\ddot{\mathbf{r}} = \frac{d\dot{\mathbf{r}}}{dt} = \frac{d}{dt}(\boldsymbol{\omega} \wedge \mathbf{r}) = \boldsymbol{\omega} \wedge \dot{\mathbf{r}} + \dot{\boldsymbol{\omega}} \wedge \mathbf{r}, \qquad \text{by (vi)},$$

$$= \boldsymbol{\omega} \wedge \dot{\mathbf{r}} \qquad \text{(since } \boldsymbol{\omega} \text{ is constant)}$$

$$= \boldsymbol{\omega} \wedge (\boldsymbol{\omega} \wedge \mathbf{r}) = (\boldsymbol{\omega} \cdot \mathbf{r})\boldsymbol{\omega} - (\boldsymbol{\omega} \cdot \boldsymbol{\omega})\mathbf{r} = -\omega^2 \mathbf{r}, \qquad (4.3)$$

provided that $\boldsymbol{\omega} \cdot \mathbf{r} = 0$. The required locus is therefore the plane through O perpendicular to $\boldsymbol{\omega}$. Each point on this plane moves uniformly around a circle with centre O and has acceleration of magnitude $\omega^2 r$ directed towards O.

(b) $\qquad d(\mathbf{r} \wedge \dot{\mathbf{r}})/dt = \mathbf{r} \wedge \ddot{\mathbf{r}} + \dot{\mathbf{r}} \wedge \dot{\mathbf{r}}$

$$= \mathbf{r} \wedge [(\boldsymbol{\omega} \cdot \mathbf{r})\boldsymbol{\omega} - \omega^2 \mathbf{r}] = (\boldsymbol{\omega} \cdot \mathbf{r})\mathbf{r} \wedge \boldsymbol{\omega},$$

by (4.3). Therefore the required locus consists of the plane through O perpendicular to $\boldsymbol{\omega}$, together with the axis of rotation (on which $\mathbf{r} \wedge \boldsymbol{\omega} = 0$). $\qquad \square$

Problem 4.7 If $\mathbf{a}$ and $\mathbf{b}$ are constant vectors, find $d|\mathbf{a} + t\mathbf{b}|/dt$.

47

Solution. Let **c** denote $\mathbf{a} + t\mathbf{b}$. Then

$$\frac{d}{dt}|\mathbf{a} + t\mathbf{b}| = \frac{d}{dt}(\mathbf{c}.\mathbf{c})^{\frac{1}{2}}$$

$$= \tfrac{1}{2}(\mathbf{c}.\mathbf{c})^{-\frac{1}{2}}(\dot{\mathbf{c}}.\mathbf{c} + \mathbf{c}.\dot{\mathbf{c}})$$

$$= \frac{\mathbf{c}.\dot{\mathbf{c}}}{(\mathbf{c}.\mathbf{c})^{\frac{1}{2}}}$$

$$= \frac{(\mathbf{a} + t\mathbf{b}).\mathbf{b}}{|\mathbf{a} + t\mathbf{b}|}. \qquad \square$$

4.2 Partial Differentiation of Vectors

If a vector **a** depends on several independent scalar variables $u, v, w, \ldots$, it is said to be a function of these variables. If it possesses a derivative with respect to u, when $v, w, \ldots$ are all kept constant, then this is called the *partial derivative* of **a** with respect to u. The partial derivative with respect to any one of the other variables $v, w, \ldots$ is defined in a similar way. As an example, the wind velocity vector **v** near the earth's surface is a function of the latitude l, the longitude m and the time t. At a fixed point (l, m) on earth, the rate of change of wind velocity with respect to time is

$$\frac{\partial \mathbf{v}}{\partial t} = \lim_{\Delta t \to 0} \frac{\mathbf{v}(l, m, t + \Delta t) - \mathbf{v}(l, m, t)}{\Delta t},$$

while at any instant of time t, the rate of change of **v** with respect to angle of latitude is

$$\frac{\partial \mathbf{v}}{\partial l} = \lim_{\Delta l \to 0} \frac{\mathbf{v}(l + \Delta l, m, t) - \mathbf{v}(l, m, t)}{\Delta l},$$

and so on.

Problem 4.8 The velocity vector **q** at any point $P(x, y, z)$ in a moving cloud of dust is a function of x, y, z and the time t. If **q** is given by

$$\mathbf{q} = xy\, e^t \mathbf{i} + zt\mathbf{j} - yt^2 \sin z\, \mathbf{k}, \qquad (4.4)$$

find $\partial \mathbf{q}/\partial z$ and $\partial \mathbf{q}/\partial t$.

Solution. Differentiation of (4.4) with respect to z, with x, y, t kept constant, gives

$$\partial \mathbf{q}/\partial z = t\mathbf{j} - yt^2 \cos z\, \mathbf{k}.$$

Similarly, differentiation with respect to t with x, y, z kept constant yields

$$\partial \mathbf{q}/\partial t = xy\, e^t \mathbf{i} + z\mathbf{j} - 2yt \sin z\, \mathbf{k}. \qquad \square$$

If $\mathbf{a} = \mathbf{a}(u, v, w, \ldots)$, where each of the variables is a function of one variable t, then $\mathbf{a}$ may be regarded as a function of t only, and the *chain rule*

$$\frac{d\mathbf{a}}{dt} = \frac{\partial \mathbf{a}}{\partial u}\frac{du}{dt} + \frac{\partial \mathbf{a}}{\partial v}\frac{dv}{dt} + \frac{\partial \mathbf{a}}{\partial w}\frac{dw}{dt} + \dots \tag{4.5}$$

applies, where $\partial \mathbf{a}/\partial u$ is formed with $v, w, \dots$ kept constant, etc. This rule is easily proved by expressing $\mathbf{a}$ in rectangular component form $\mathbf{a} = a_1\mathbf{i} + a_2\mathbf{j} + a_3\mathbf{k}$, and applying standard rules of calculus to each of the functions a_1, a_2, a_3.

Problem 4.9 If $\mathbf{a} = uv^3\mathbf{i} - vw\mathbf{j} + 2u^2w^3\mathbf{k}$, and $u = t$, $v = t^3$, $w = 2t^2$, find $d\mathbf{a}/dt$ when $t = 1$.

Solution. We have

$$du/dt = 1, \quad dv/dt = 3t^2, \quad dw/dt = 4t.$$

and therefore

$$\frac{d\mathbf{a}}{dt} = \frac{\partial \mathbf{a}}{\partial u}\frac{du}{dt} + \frac{\partial \mathbf{a}}{\partial v}\frac{dv}{dt} + \frac{\partial \mathbf{a}}{\partial w}\frac{dw}{dt}$$

$$= (v^3\mathbf{i} + 4uw^3\mathbf{k}) + (3uv^2\mathbf{i} - w\mathbf{j})3t^2 + (-v\mathbf{j} + 6u^2w^2\mathbf{k})4t.$$

This gives, when $t = 1$,

$$d\mathbf{a}/dt = 10\mathbf{i} - 10\mathbf{j} + 128\mathbf{k}.$$

Alternatively, in this rather simple example we might substitute in $\mathbf{a}$ for u, v, w in terms of t before differentiation. ☐

Problem 4.10 If $\mathbf{a} = e^{xy}\mathbf{i} - y\sin x\,\mathbf{k}$, and $s = xy$, $t = x^2 - y^2$, find $\partial \mathbf{a}/\partial s$ (with t constant) when $s = 1$, $t = 0$.

Solution. It would be complicated here to substitute for x and y, in $\mathbf{a}$, in terms of s and t. Evidently, by (4.5) we have

$$\frac{\partial \mathbf{a}}{\partial s} = \frac{\partial \mathbf{a}}{\partial x}\frac{\partial x}{\partial s} + \frac{\partial \mathbf{a}}{\partial y}\frac{\partial y}{\partial s}. \tag{4.6}$$

But if t is kept constant we have also

$$\frac{\partial s}{\partial s} = 1 = \frac{\partial s}{\partial x}\frac{\partial x}{\partial s} + \frac{\partial s}{\partial y}\frac{\partial y}{\partial s} = y\frac{\partial x}{\partial s} + x\frac{\partial y}{\partial s},$$

$$\frac{\partial t}{\partial s} = 0 = \frac{\partial t}{\partial x}\frac{\partial x}{\partial s} + \frac{\partial t}{\partial y}\frac{\partial y}{\partial s} = 2x\frac{\partial x}{\partial s} - 2y\frac{\partial y}{\partial s}.$$

Solving,

$$\partial x/\partial s = y/(x^2 + y^2), \quad \partial y/\partial s = x/(x^2 + y^2). \tag{4.7}$$

Now, $\quad \partial \mathbf{a}/\partial x = ye^{xy}\mathbf{i} - y\cos x\,\mathbf{k}, \quad \partial \mathbf{a}/\partial y = xe^{xy}\mathbf{i} - \sin x\,\mathbf{k}, \tag{4.8}$

which enables us, together with (4.6), (4.7), to find $\partial \mathbf{a}/\partial s$ as a function of x and y.

When $s = 1$ and $t = 0$, possible values of x and y are $x = y = \pm 1$. For either choice of sign, it is found on substitution of these values that

$$\partial\mathbf{a}/\partial s = e\mathbf{i} - \tfrac{1}{2}[\sin(1) + \cos(1)]\mathbf{k}. \qquad \square$$

Problem 4.11 Find the acceleration at time $t = 0$ of the particle which is then passing through the point $(1, 2, 0)$ in the dust cloud of Problem 4.8.

Solution. In (4.4), the variables x, y, z were to be regarded as independent of one another and of the time t. Let us now restrict x, y and z to be the coordinates of the particular dust particle P in question. Then they are functions of t; and $dx/dt, dy/dt, dz/dt$ are the components of the velocity vector $\mathbf{q}$ for the particle.

Along the path of P, its velocity is changing at the rate $d\mathbf{q}/dt$, where by the chain rule (*c.f.* (4.5)), since $dt/dt = 1$,

$$\frac{d\mathbf{q}}{dt} = \frac{\partial\mathbf{q}}{\partial x}\frac{dx}{dt} + \frac{\partial\mathbf{q}}{\partial y}\frac{dy}{dt} + \frac{\partial\mathbf{q}}{\partial z}\frac{dz}{dt} + \frac{\partial\mathbf{q}}{\partial t}$$

$$= xye^t\frac{\partial\mathbf{q}}{\partial x} + zt\frac{\partial\mathbf{q}}{\partial y} - yt^2\sin z\frac{\partial\mathbf{q}}{\partial z} + \frac{\partial\mathbf{q}}{\partial t}.$$

When $(x, y, z) = (1, 2, 0)$, and $t = 0$,

$$\frac{\partial\mathbf{q}}{\partial x} = 2\mathbf{i}, \quad \frac{\partial\mathbf{q}}{\partial y} = \mathbf{i}, \quad \frac{\partial\mathbf{q}}{\partial z} = 0, \quad \frac{\partial\mathbf{q}}{\partial t} = 2\mathbf{i},$$

and so

$$d\mathbf{q}/dt = 6\mathbf{i},$$

which is the instantaneous acceleration of the particle at the point $(1, 2, 0)$ at time $t = 0$. $\qquad \square$

4.3 Integration with Respect to One Scalar Variable If $\mathbf{b}(u)$ is a vector function of the scalar variable u, possessing a derivative

$$\mathbf{a}(u) = d\mathbf{b}/du,$$

then $\mathbf{b}(u)$ is called an *indefinite integral* of $\mathbf{a}(u)$, and we write

$$\mathbf{b}(u) = \int \mathbf{a}(u)\, du.$$

The indefinite integral of a given vector $\mathbf{a}(u)$, when it exists, is defined only to within an arbitrary additive constant vector.

If $\mathbf{a}(u) = a_1(u)\mathbf{i} + a_2(u)\mathbf{j} + a_3(u)\mathbf{k}$, then

$$\int \mathbf{a}(u)\, du = \mathbf{i}\int a_1(u)\, du + \mathbf{j}\int a_2(u)\, du + \mathbf{k}\int a_3(u)\, du. \qquad (4.9)$$

Problem 4.12 If **c** is a constant vector, and **a** = **a**(u), evaluate

$$\int \mathbf{c} \wedge \frac{d\mathbf{a}}{du} \, du.$$

Solution. Since **c** is constant,

$$\frac{d}{du}(\mathbf{c} \wedge \mathbf{a}) = \mathbf{c} \wedge \frac{d\mathbf{a}}{du},$$

Hence

$$\int \mathbf{c} \wedge \frac{d\mathbf{a}}{du} \, du = \mathbf{c} \wedge \mathbf{a} + \mathbf{b},$$

where **b** is an arbitrary constant vector. $\square$

Problem 4.13 Evaluate the following indefinite integrals with respect to t, where **r** = **r**(t), $\dot{\mathbf{r}} = d\mathbf{r}/dt$, and **a** is a constant vector; (i) $\mathbf{r} \wedge \ddot{\mathbf{r}}$, (ii) $\mathbf{r} \cdot \dot{\mathbf{r}}$, (iii) $\mathbf{a} \cdot (\mathbf{r} \wedge \ddot{\mathbf{r}})$.

Solution. (i) $d(\mathbf{r} \wedge \dot{\mathbf{r}})/dt = \mathbf{r} \wedge \ddot{\mathbf{r}} + \dot{\mathbf{r}} \wedge \dot{\mathbf{r}} = \mathbf{r} \wedge \ddot{\mathbf{r}}$, and therefore

$$\int \mathbf{r} \wedge \ddot{\mathbf{r}} \, dt = \mathbf{r} \wedge \dot{\mathbf{r}} + \mathbf{c},$$

where **c** is an arbitrary constant vector.

(ii) $d(\mathbf{r} \cdot \mathbf{r})/dt = 2\mathbf{r} \cdot \dot{\mathbf{r}}$, and therefore

$$\int \mathbf{r} \cdot \dot{\mathbf{r}} \, dt = \tfrac{1}{2}\mathbf{r} \cdot \mathbf{r} + c = \tfrac{1}{2}r^2 + c.$$

(iii) Because **a** is constant,

$$\frac{d}{dt}\left[\mathbf{a} \cdot (\mathbf{r} \wedge \dot{\mathbf{r}})\right] = \mathbf{a} \cdot \frac{d}{dt}(\mathbf{r} \wedge \dot{\mathbf{r}}) = \mathbf{a} \cdot (\mathbf{r} \wedge \ddot{\mathbf{r}}),$$

and hence

$$\int \mathbf{a} \cdot (\mathbf{r} \wedge \ddot{\mathbf{r}}) \, dt = \mathbf{a} \cdot (\mathbf{r} \wedge \dot{\mathbf{r}}) + c. \quad \square$$

Problem 4.14 Evaluate $\displaystyle\int_0^1 \mathbf{a}(u) \, du$, where $\mathbf{a}(u) = e^u \mathbf{i} + \sin u \cos u \, \mathbf{j} - 2u^2 \mathbf{k}$.

Solution. We have, by (4.9)

$$\int_0^1 \mathbf{a}(u) \, du = \left[e^u \mathbf{i} + \tfrac{1}{2} \sin^2 u \, \mathbf{j} - \tfrac{2}{3} u^3 \mathbf{k} \right]_0^1$$

$$= (e-1)\mathbf{i} + \tfrac{1}{2} \sin^2 1 \, \mathbf{j} - \tfrac{2}{3}\mathbf{k}. \quad \square$$

EXERCISES

1. Given $\mathbf{a} = t^3 \mathbf{i} - 2t \mathbf{j} + t^2 \mathbf{k}$, $\mathbf{b} = \cos t \, \mathbf{i} + \sin t \, \mathbf{j} + \mathbf{k}$, find $d(\mathbf{a} \cdot \mathbf{b})/dt$ and $d(\mathbf{a} \wedge \mathbf{b})/dt$. Verify your results using a second method.

2. If $\mathbf{r} = \mathbf{r}(t)$, show that at $t = 0$,

$$\frac{d}{dt}\left|\dot{\mathbf{r}} + t^2\mathbf{r}\right| = \frac{\dot{\mathbf{r}} \cdot \ddot{\mathbf{r}}}{|\dot{\mathbf{r}}|}$$

3. The position vector of a particle relative to the origin, at time t, is

$$\mathbf{r} = (\omega t \sin \omega t + \cos \omega t)\mathbf{i} + (\sin \omega t - \omega t \cos \omega t)\mathbf{j},$$

where ω is a constant. (i) Find the velocity and acceleration at any time; (ii) show that the acceleration is in the direction of $\mathbf{r}$ at the time $t = 0$ (and only then), and find the resolute of acceleration in the direction of $\mathbf{r}$ at $t = 1$.

4. If $\mathbf{a} = v \cos u\mathbf{i} - u \cos v\mathbf{j} + u^2v\mathbf{k}$, find $\partial\mathbf{a}/\partial u$, $\partial\mathbf{a}/\partial v$, $\partial^2\mathbf{a}/\partial u^2$ at $u = 0$, $v = \pi$.

5. If $\mathbf{a} = ze^{2x}\mathbf{i} - xz \sin z\mathbf{j} + x^2 \cos z\mathbf{k}$, and $u = e^x \cos z$, $v = e^x \sin z$, find $\partial\mathbf{a}/\partial u$ (v constant) and $\partial\mathbf{a}/\partial v$ (u constant) at $x = 0$, $z = \frac{1}{2}\pi$.

6. In a moving fluid, the velocity of the particle passing through the general point $P(x, y, z)$, at time t, is

$$\mathbf{v} = x^2(1+t)\mathbf{i} - yz(1-t)\mathbf{j} + 2xyz^2\, t\mathbf{k}.$$

Show that, at $t = 0$, the locus of points at which the acceleration of the particle is parallel to its velocity form the coordinate planes $x = 0$, $y = 0$. $z = 0$.

7. Evaluate $\displaystyle\int_0^{\pi/2} \mathbf{a}\, dt$, where $\mathbf{a} = 2 \cos t\,\mathbf{i} - e^t \sin t\,\mathbf{j} + 2te^t\,\mathbf{k}$.

8. If $\mathbf{r} = \mathbf{r}(t)$ and $\mathbf{a}$ is a constant vector, find the indefinite integrals with respect to t of

(i) $\dfrac{1}{r}\dot{\mathbf{r}} - \dfrac{1}{r^2}\dot{r}\mathbf{r}$; (ii) $(\mathbf{r} \wedge \dot{\mathbf{r}}) \cdot \ddot{\mathbf{r}}$; (iii) $(\mathbf{a} \cdot \dot{\mathbf{r}})\mathbf{r} \wedge \dot{\mathbf{r}} + (\mathbf{a} \cdot \mathbf{r})\mathbf{r} \wedge \ddot{\mathbf{r}}$.

9. Show that the general solutions of the differential equations for $\mathbf{r}(t)$:

(i) $\ddot{\mathbf{r}} - 4\mathbf{r} = 0$, (ii) $\ddot{\mathbf{r}} + 2\dot{\mathbf{r}} + \mathbf{r} = 0$

are $\mathbf{r} = \mathbf{A}e^{2t} + \mathbf{B}e^{-2t}$ and $\mathbf{r} = e^{-t}(\mathbf{A} + \mathbf{B}t)$ respectively, where $\mathbf{A}$ and $\mathbf{B}$ are arbitrary constant vectors.

10. Find the solution for $\mathbf{r}(t)$ of the differential equation $\ddot{\mathbf{r}} - 4\mathbf{r} = 4t\mathbf{a}$. where $\mathbf{a}$ is a constant vector, given that $\mathbf{r} = \dot{\mathbf{r}} = 0$ at $t = 0$.

Chapter 5

Differential Geometry of Curves and Surfaces

5.1. Geometry of Space Curves   Let $\mathbf{r} = \mathbf{r}(s)$ be the equation of a curve C in three-dimensional space, where s is the arc length measured along the curve from a fixed point A to the point $P(\mathbf{r})$. If P' is a point on the curve near P, with parameter $s + \Delta s$, then the vector

$$\mathbf{t} = \lim_{\Delta s \to 0} \frac{\mathbf{PP'}}{\Delta s}$$

is the *unit* tangent vector at P in the direction of s increasing. Since $\mathbf{t}$ is a unit vector,

$$\frac{d}{ds}(\mathbf{t} \cdot \mathbf{t}) = 0 = 2\mathbf{t} \cdot \frac{d\mathbf{t}}{ds},$$

which shows that dt/ds is perpendicular to $\mathbf{t}$. In Fig. 5.1, the unit tangent vectors at P and P' are drawn with the origin as common initial point,

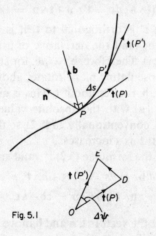

Fig. 5.1

$\Delta\psi$ being the angle through which $\mathbf{t}$ turns between the points P and P'. Now,

$$\frac{d\psi}{ds} = \lim_{\Delta s \to 0} \frac{\Delta\psi}{\Delta s} = \lim_{\Delta s \to 0} \frac{DE}{\Delta s} = \left| \frac{d\mathbf{t}}{ds} \right|, \qquad (5.1)$$

since DE is the increment $\Delta \mathbf{t}$ in $\mathbf{t}$ corresponding to the increment Δs in s. Therefore, (5.1) represents the rate of rotation of the tangent vector with respect to arc distance.

Write $dt/ds = \kappa\mathbf{n}$, where $\mathbf{n}$ is a unit vector in the limiting direction of DE. This direction is normal to the tangent at P, and lies in the limiting plane of the tangents at P and P', the latter being known as the *osculating plane* at P, while the positive (or zero) number κ is the *curvature* at P. The vector $\mathbf{n}$ defines the direction of the *principal normal* at this point.

The direction of the *binormal* at P is that of the unit vector $\mathbf{b} = \mathbf{t} \wedge \mathbf{n}$, so that $\mathbf{t}, \mathbf{n}, \mathbf{b}$ form a right-handed orthogonal set of unit vectors, of which the first two lie in the osculating plane (Fig. 5.1).

Problem 5.1 (*Serret–Frenet formulae.*) Prove that

$$
\begin{aligned}
\mathbf{t}' &= && \kappa\mathbf{n} \\
\mathbf{n}' &= -\kappa\mathbf{t} && &&+\tau\mathbf{b} \\
\mathbf{b}' &= && -\tau\mathbf{n}
\end{aligned}
\tag{5.2}
$$

where a prime denotes differentiation with respect to s, and the *torsion* τ is the rate at which the osculating plane rotates about the tangent vector as s increases.

Solution. The first of these formulae has already been obtained. For the third,

$$\mathbf{b}' = d(\mathbf{t}\wedge\mathbf{n})/ds = \mathbf{t}'\wedge\mathbf{n} + \mathbf{t}\wedge\mathbf{n}' = \mathbf{t}\wedge\mathbf{n}',$$

since $\mathbf{t}' = \kappa\mathbf{n}$. Therefore $\mathbf{b}'$ is orthogonal to $\mathbf{t}$; it is also orthogonal to $\mathbf{b}$ because $\mathbf{b}$ is a unit vector (and the derivative of a unit vector is always orthogonal to that vector). Therefore, $\mathbf{b}' = \mu\mathbf{n}$, for some real number μ.

The rate at which the osculating plane rotates about $\mathbf{t}$ is the same as the rate at which its normal, $\mathbf{b}$, rotates about $\mathbf{t}$. This is given in magnitude by $|d\mathbf{b}/ds|$, which identifies $|\mu|$ with the absolute value of the torsion. The minus sign is introduced, conventionally, in (5.2), so that τ is positive when $\mathbf{b}$ rotates positively about $\mathbf{t}$ as s increases.

Finally, the second of the formulae (5.2) is valid since

$$
\begin{aligned}
\mathbf{n}' &= d(\mathbf{b}\wedge\mathbf{t})/ds = \mathbf{b}'\wedge\mathbf{t} + \mathbf{b}\wedge\mathbf{t}' \\
&= -\tau\mathbf{n}\wedge\mathbf{t} + \mathbf{b}\wedge\kappa\mathbf{n} = \tau\mathbf{b} - \kappa\mathbf{t}. \qquad \square
\end{aligned}
$$

Problem 5.2 Show that the vectors $\mathbf{t}, \mathbf{n}$ and $\mathbf{b}$ move as though embedded in a rigid body as the point P moves along the space curve. Find the angular velocity of this body if P moves at unit speed.

Solution. The first result is evident since each vector is of constant length and the angle between any pair is constant. Let $\boldsymbol{\omega}$ be the angular velocity of the rigid body. Since s increases at the same rate as the time as P travels along the curve (in the direction s increasing), $\boldsymbol{\omega}$ has to satisfy (*c.f.* Problem 1.37)

$$d\mathbf{t}/ds = \boldsymbol{\omega}\wedge\mathbf{t} = \kappa\mathbf{n}, \tag{5.3}$$

$$\mathbf{dn}/ds = \boldsymbol{\omega} \wedge \mathbf{n} = -\kappa \mathbf{t} + \tau \mathbf{b}, \tag{5.4}$$

$$\mathbf{db}/ds = \boldsymbol{\omega} \wedge \mathbf{b} = -\tau \mathbf{n}. \tag{5.5}$$

Now, $\kappa \mathbf{n} = \kappa \mathbf{b} \wedge \mathbf{t}$, and hence (5.3) is satisfied if $\boldsymbol{\omega} = \kappa \mathbf{b} + \alpha \mathbf{t}$, where α is arbitrary. Substituting this expression for $\boldsymbol{\omega}$ in (5.4), we find

$$(\kappa \mathbf{b} + \alpha \mathbf{t}) \wedge \mathbf{n} = -\kappa \mathbf{t} + \tau \mathbf{b} = -\kappa \mathbf{t} + \alpha \mathbf{b},$$

whence $\alpha = \tau$. This determines $\boldsymbol{\omega}$ uniquely as

$$\boldsymbol{\omega} = \kappa \mathbf{b} + \tau \mathbf{t}.$$

It is easily verified that this expression for $\boldsymbol{\omega}$ satisfies (5.5), also. ☐

Problem 5.3 If C is the curve $x = x(u)$, $y = y(u)$, $z = z(u)$, where u is a parameter which increases continuously as the curve is described in one direction, find an expression for the unit tangent vector pointing in this direction.

Solution. Let $\mathbf{r}(u) = x(u)\mathbf{i} + y(u)\mathbf{j} + z(u)\mathbf{k}$ be the position vector, relative to the origin, of the point P with parameter u on C. If s denotes arc distance along C from a fixed point, in the direction u increasing, then the unit tangent vector in this sense is

$$\mathbf{t} = \frac{d\mathbf{r}}{ds} = \frac{d\mathbf{r}}{du}\frac{du}{ds}.$$

But if ds and du are both positive, then $ds = |d\mathbf{r}|$, and $ds/du = |d\mathbf{r}/du|$. Therefore,

$$\frac{du}{ds} = \left(\frac{ds}{du}\right)^{-1} = \left|\frac{d\mathbf{r}}{du}\right|^{-1},$$

and

$$\mathbf{t} = \left(\frac{d\mathbf{r}}{du}\right)\bigg/\left|\frac{d\mathbf{r}}{du}\right|. \tag{5.6}$$

In terms of rectangular components this becomes

$$\mathbf{t} = \left(\frac{dx}{du}\mathbf{i} + \frac{dy}{du}\mathbf{j} + \frac{dz}{du}\mathbf{k}\right)\bigg/\left[\left(\frac{dx}{du}\right)^2 + \left(\frac{dy}{du}\right)^2 + \left(\frac{dz}{du}\right)^2\right]^{\frac{1}{2}}. \qquad ☐ \tag{5.7}$$

Problem 5.4 Find the unit tangent vector and the curvature at a general point of the circular helix:

$$x = \cos u, \quad y = \sin u, \quad z = u.$$

Solution. Since these equations imply $x^2 + y^2 = 1$, the curve lies on the cylinder of unit radius which has its axis along Oz. If N is the projection of the point $P(u)$ on the xy plane, it follows that $u = \tan^{-1}(y/x)$ is the angle NOx, to within the addition of a multiple of 2π. Also, z increases along the curve at a constant rate relative to the angle u, and so we see that the curve is, indeed, a circular helix.

Put $\mathbf{r} = x\mathbf{i} + y\mathbf{j} + z\mathbf{k}$. Then

$$\frac{d\mathbf{r}}{du} = \frac{dx}{du}\mathbf{i} + \frac{dy}{du}\mathbf{j} + \frac{dz}{du}\mathbf{k}$$

$$= -\sin u\,\mathbf{i} + \cos u\,\mathbf{j} + \mathbf{k},$$

and therefore the unit tangent vector in the direction u increasing is, by (5.6),

$$\mathbf{t} = \frac{d\mathbf{r}}{du}\Big/\left|\frac{d\mathbf{r}}{du}\right| = \frac{1}{\sqrt{2}}(-\sin u\,\mathbf{i} + \cos u\,\mathbf{j} + \mathbf{k})$$

at the point $P(u)$. The principal normal $\mathbf{n}$ satisfies (5.3), so that by differentiation,

$$\kappa\mathbf{n} = \frac{d\mathbf{t}}{ds} = \frac{d\mathbf{t}}{du}\frac{du}{ds} = \frac{d\mathbf{t}}{du}\Big/\left|\frac{d\mathbf{r}}{du}\right|$$

$$= \tfrac{1}{2}(-\cos u\,\mathbf{i} - \sin u\,\mathbf{j}). \tag{5.8}$$

Since κ is positive, dividing by $|d\mathbf{t}/ds|$ gives the required unit vector

$$\mathbf{n} = -\cos u\,\mathbf{i} - \sin u\,\mathbf{j}.$$

We note that the principal normal vector is parallel to the xy plane and is directed towards Oz, since it is opposed to the vector $\mathbf{ON} = \cos u\,\mathbf{i} + \sin u\,\mathbf{j}$.

The curvature κ is determined by taking moduli in (5.8),

$$\kappa = |d\mathbf{t}/ds| = \tfrac{1}{2}. \qquad \square$$

Problem 5.5 Find the binormal $\mathbf{b}$ and the torsion τ at a general point $P(u)$ of the circular helix in the last problem.

Solution. We have, using the values obtained for $\mathbf{t}$ and $\mathbf{n}$,

$$\mathbf{b} = \mathbf{t} \wedge \mathbf{n} = \frac{1}{\sqrt{2}}\begin{vmatrix} \mathbf{i} & \mathbf{j} & \mathbf{k} \\ -\sin u & \cos u & 1 \\ -\cos u & -\sin u & 0 \end{vmatrix}$$

$$= (1/\sqrt{2})(\sin u\,\mathbf{i} - \cos u\,\mathbf{j} + \mathbf{k}). \tag{5.9}$$

Also, by (5.5),

$$\frac{d\mathbf{b}}{ds} = \frac{d\mathbf{b}}{du}\frac{du}{ds} = \frac{d\mathbf{b}}{du}\Big/\left|\frac{d\mathbf{r}}{du}\right| = -\tau\mathbf{n}. \tag{5.10}$$

Differentiating (5.9), we get (since $|d\mathbf{r}/du| = 1/\sqrt{2}$)

$$d\mathbf{b}/ds = \cos u\,\mathbf{i} + \sin u\,\mathbf{j}.$$

Comparison with (5.10) and the value found for $\mathbf{n}$, gives $\tau = 1$. $\qquad \square$

Problem 5.6 Find the equations of the osculating plane and the *rectifying plane* at the point $Q(u = \tfrac{1}{2}\pi)$ on the circular helix in the last two problems.

Solution. The normal to the osculating plane at Q is parallel to the vector

56

b, where (on putting $u = \frac{1}{2}\pi$ in (5.9)) we have

$$\mathbf{b} = (1/\sqrt{2})(\mathbf{i}+\mathbf{k}).$$

The position vector of the point Q is

$$\mathbf{q} = \cos u\,\mathbf{i}+\sin u\,\mathbf{j}+u\mathbf{k} = \mathbf{j}+\tfrac{1}{2}\pi\mathbf{k},$$

and since the osculating plane at Q contains this point its equation is

$$\mathbf{r}\cdot\mathbf{b} = \mathbf{q}\cdot\mathbf{b},$$

i.e.
$$\mathbf{r}\cdot(\mathbf{i}+\mathbf{k}) = \tfrac{1}{2}\pi,$$

or
$$x+z = \tfrac{1}{2}\pi, \qquad \text{in cartesian form.}$$

The *rectifying plane* at the point Q is defined to be the plane which passes through Q and is parallel to the vectors **b** and **t** at this point. The principal normal at Q is

$$\mathbf{n} = -\cos u\,\mathbf{i}-\sin u\,\mathbf{j} = -\mathbf{j},$$

and since this is orthogonal to **b** and **t** it is normal to the rectifying plane, which therefore has the equation

$$\mathbf{r}\cdot\mathbf{n} = \mathbf{q}\cdot\mathbf{n},$$

i.e.
$$\mathbf{r}\cdot\mathbf{j} = 1,$$

or
$$y = 1, \qquad \text{in cartesian form.} \qquad \square$$

Problem 5.7 Show that the curvature at any point of a circle is $\kappa = 1/\rho$, where ρ is the radius.

Solution. Evidently, we may suppose the circle to lie in the xy plane with the origin as centre. The parametric form is then

$$x = \rho\cos\theta, \quad y = \rho\sin\theta, \quad z = 0, \qquad (0 \leqslant \theta \leqslant 2\pi).$$

The arc distance in the direction θ increasing, measured from $\theta = 0$, is $s = \rho\theta$, and therefore

$$\mathbf{t} = \frac{d\mathbf{r}}{ds} = \frac{d\mathbf{r}}{d\theta}\frac{d\theta}{ds} = (-\rho\sin\theta\,\mathbf{i}+\rho\cos\theta\,\mathbf{j})/\rho$$
$$= -\sin\theta\,\mathbf{i}+\cos\theta\,\mathbf{j},$$

and
$$\frac{d\mathbf{t}}{ds} = \frac{d\mathbf{t}}{d\theta}\frac{d\theta}{ds} = \frac{1}{\rho}(-\cos\theta\,\mathbf{i}-\sin\theta\,\mathbf{j}).$$

On taking moduli we get, by the first of (5.2),

$$\kappa = \left|\frac{d\mathbf{t}}{ds}\right| = \frac{1}{\rho}. \qquad \square$$

Problem 5.8 Express the curve of intersection of the surfaces

$$xz = y^2, \quad xy = z \qquad (5.11)$$

in parametric form, and find the *radius of curvature* at the point $(1, 1, 1)$.

57

Solution. The choice of parameter may be made in a variety of ways. For simplicity, we shall take x as the parameter u. Multiplication of equations (5.11) together gives

$$x^2yz = y^2z,$$

i.e.
$$x^2 = y, \qquad\qquad (5.12)$$

provided that neither y nor z vanishes. By (5.11) if one of the variables y or z is equal to zero, then so is the other, and it follows that the curve of intersection of the surfaces consists of two parts;

the x axis: $\quad x = u, \quad y = 0, \quad z = 0,$

and the cubic: $\quad x = u, \quad y = u^2, \quad z = u^3, \qquad (5.13)$

where we have used (5.12) and the second of (5.11).

The *radius of curvature* ρ at a point Q on a curve is the radius of the circle which most closely fits the curve at that point. Such a circle lies in the osculating plane, touches the curve at Q, and has the same curvature as the curve at this point. Thus, by Problem 5.7, it follows that the relation $\kappa = 1/\rho$ is valid for curves in general.

The branch containing the point $(1, 1, 1)$ is the cubic (5.13), and the tangent vector at a general point with parameter u, on this branch, has the direction of the vector

$$\frac{d\mathbf{r}}{du} = \frac{dx}{du}\mathbf{i} + \frac{dy}{du}\mathbf{j} + \frac{dz}{du}\mathbf{k} = \mathbf{i} + 2u\mathbf{j} + 3u^2\mathbf{k}.$$

Therefore the unit tangent vector in the direction u increasing is

$$\mathbf{t} = \frac{d\mathbf{r}/du}{|d\mathbf{r}/du|} = (1 + 4u^2 + 9u^4)^{-\frac{1}{2}}(\mathbf{i} + 2u\mathbf{j} + 3u^2\mathbf{k}).$$

Differentiating,

$$d\mathbf{t}/du = (1 + 4u^2 + 9u^4)^{-\frac{1}{2}}(2\mathbf{j} + 6u\mathbf{k})$$
$$- \tfrac{1}{2}(1 + 4u^2 + 9u^4)^{-\frac{3}{2}}(8u + 36u^3)(\mathbf{i} + 2u\mathbf{j} + 3u^2\mathbf{k}).$$

At the point $(1, 1, 1)$, we have $u = 1$, and

$$\frac{d\mathbf{t}}{du} = \frac{1}{(14)^{\frac{3}{2}}}[14(2\mathbf{j} + 6\mathbf{k}) - \tfrac{1}{2}(44)(\mathbf{i} + 2\mathbf{j} + 3\mathbf{k})]$$

$$= \frac{1}{7\sqrt{14}}(-11\mathbf{i} - 8\mathbf{j} + 9\mathbf{k}).$$

Also, $ds/du = |d\mathbf{r}/du| = \sqrt{14}$ at $u = 1$. Dividing,

$$\frac{d\mathbf{t}}{ds} = \frac{d\mathbf{t}/du}{ds/du} = \frac{1}{98}(-11\mathbf{i} - 8\mathbf{j} + 9\mathbf{k}).$$

By the first of (5.2), $|d\mathbf{t}/ds| = \kappa = 1/\rho$, giving

$$\rho = \frac{98}{\sqrt{266}} = \frac{7}{19}\sqrt{266}$$

at the point $(1, 1, 1)$. $\square$

Problem 5.9 Prove the formula

$$\rho^2 \mathbf{r}' \cdot (\mathbf{r}'' \wedge \mathbf{r}''') = \tau,$$

where a prime denotes differentiation with respect to s.

Solution. We have $\mathbf{r}' = \mathbf{t}$, and so by the first of (5.2),

$$\mathbf{r}' \wedge \mathbf{r}'' = \mathbf{t} \wedge \mathbf{t}' = \mathbf{t} \wedge \kappa \mathbf{n} = \kappa \mathbf{b} = \rho^{-1}\mathbf{b},$$

thus $$\mathbf{b}' = \frac{d}{ds}[(\rho(\mathbf{r}' \wedge \mathbf{r}''))] = \rho'(\mathbf{r}' \wedge \mathbf{r}'') + \rho(\mathbf{r}' \wedge \mathbf{r}''').$$

But, by (5.2), $\mathbf{b}' = -\tau\mathbf{n}$, giving

$$\tau = -\mathbf{n} \cdot \mathbf{b}' = -\mathbf{n} \cdot [\rho(\mathbf{r}' \wedge \mathbf{r}''')],$$

since $\mathbf{n} \cdot (\mathbf{r}' \wedge \mathbf{r}'') = \mathbf{n} \cdot \kappa \mathbf{b} = 0$. Writing $\mathbf{n} = \mathbf{t}'/\kappa = \rho\mathbf{t}' = \rho\mathbf{r}''$, we get

$$\tau = -\rho^2 \mathbf{r}'' \cdot (\mathbf{r}' \wedge \mathbf{r}''') = \rho^2 \mathbf{r}' \cdot (\mathbf{r}'' \wedge \mathbf{r}'''). \qquad \square$$

5.2 Surfaces A surface in three-dimensional space is a set of points $\mathbf{r} = \mathbf{r}(u, v)$ which depend on two independent parameters u and v. In rectangular cartesian coordinates we have

$$x = x(u, v), \quad y = y(u, v), \quad z = z(u, v), \tag{5.14}$$

or on eliminating u and v, a single equation

$$F(x, y, z) = 0. \tag{5.15}$$

Conversely, an equation of this form can generally (though not always) be solved, in principle, for one of the coordinates in terms of the other two, which may be taken as parameters. It follows that, in general, (5.15) is the equation of a surface.

We call u and v *parametric* or *curvilinear coordinates* for the surface. The two families of lines (curves) traced on the surface as, in turn, one of the curvilinear coordinates is allowed to vary while the other is kept constant, are called *parametric lines* or *coordinate lines*. For example, the parametric line $v = v_0 = $ const. is the curve

$$x = x(u, v_0), \quad y = y(u, v_0), \quad z = z(u, v_0).$$

A tangent vector to this curve in the sense u increasing is in the direction

$$\frac{\partial \mathbf{r}}{\partial u} = \frac{\partial x}{\partial u}\mathbf{i} + \frac{\partial y}{\partial u}\mathbf{j} + \frac{\partial z}{\partial u}\mathbf{k}, \tag{5.16}$$

where the notation of partial differentiation is used to denote that the parametric coordinate, v, is held constant (at the value v_0) when we differentiate (5.14) with respect to u. Similarly, at a general point on the parametric line $u = u_0 = $ const., the direction of a tangent vector in the sense v increasing is given by

$$\frac{\partial \mathbf{r}}{\partial v} = \frac{\partial x}{\partial v}\mathbf{i} + \frac{\partial y}{\partial v}\mathbf{j} + \frac{\partial z}{\partial v}\mathbf{k}, \tag{5.17}$$

with u held constant (at the value u_0) during the differentiation. The tangent plane at any point on the surface contains both of the tangent vectors $\partial \mathbf{r}/\partial u$ and $\partial \mathbf{r}/\partial v$ to the parametric lines through that point.

Problem 5.10 Find the unit tangent vectors $\mathbf{t}_1$ and $\mathbf{t}_2$ to the parametric lines $v = $ const. and $u = $ const. at the point $P(1, 1, 1)$ on the surface

$$x = u, \quad y = v, \quad z = 1/uv, \quad (u, v \text{ positive}). \tag{5.18}$$

Solution. The equation of the surface can be written in the alternative forms $xy = 1/z$ or, more symmetrically, $xyz = 1$. The surface is thus seen to meet any plane $z = $ const. (>0) in a rectangular hyperbola. By symmetry, it follows that the surface is as shown in Fig. 5.2.

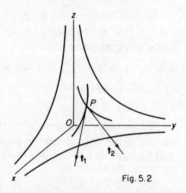

Fig. 5.2

By (5.18),

$$\frac{\partial \mathbf{r}}{\partial u} = \frac{\partial}{\partial u}(u)\mathbf{i} + \frac{\partial}{\partial u}(v)\mathbf{j} + \frac{\partial}{\partial u}\left(\frac{1}{uv}\right)\mathbf{k}$$

$$= \mathbf{i} - \frac{1}{u^2 v}\mathbf{k} = \mathbf{i} - \mathbf{k},$$

when $u = v = 1$, corresponding to the point $P(1, 1, 1)$. The *unit* vector in this direction is

$$\mathbf{t}_1 = \frac{1}{\sqrt{2}}(\mathbf{i} - \mathbf{k}).$$

Similarly,

$$\frac{\partial \mathbf{r}}{\partial v} = \frac{\partial}{\partial v}(u)\mathbf{i} + \frac{\partial}{\partial v}(v)\mathbf{j} + \frac{\partial}{\partial v}\left(\frac{1}{uv}\right)\mathbf{k}$$

$$= \mathbf{j} - \frac{1}{uv^2}\mathbf{k} = \mathbf{j} - \mathbf{k},$$

at the point P, and the *unit* tangent vector in this direction is

$$\mathbf{t}_2 = (1/\sqrt{2})(\mathbf{j} - \mathbf{k}). \qquad \square$$

Problem 5.11   Find a vector normal to the surface in Problem 5.10, at the point $Q(u = \frac{1}{2}, v = \frac{1}{3})$.

Solution. The tangent plane at Q contains the two vectors

$$\frac{\partial \mathbf{r}}{\partial u} = \mathbf{i} - \frac{1}{u^2 v}\mathbf{k} = \mathbf{i} - 12\mathbf{k},$$

$$\frac{\partial \mathbf{r}}{\partial v} = \mathbf{j} - \frac{1}{uv^2}\mathbf{k} = \mathbf{j} - 18\mathbf{k}.$$

The normal to the surface at Q is orthogonal to both these vectors, and hence is parallel to the vector

$$\frac{\partial \mathbf{r}}{\partial u} \wedge \frac{\partial \mathbf{r}}{\partial v} = (\mathbf{i} - 12\mathbf{k}) \wedge (\mathbf{j} - 18\mathbf{k}) = 12\mathbf{i} + 18\mathbf{j} + \mathbf{k}.$$

Alternatively, we can argue as follows. The equation of the surface (5.18) can be written:

$$F(x, y, z) \equiv xyz - 1 = 0.$$

If we regard x, y, and z as functions of u and v, and differentiate with respect to u while keeping v constant, we have by the chain rule of partial differentiation

$$\left(\frac{\partial F}{\partial u}\right)_{v = \text{const.}} = \frac{\partial F}{\partial x}\frac{\partial x}{\partial u} + \frac{\partial F}{\partial y}\frac{\partial y}{\partial u} + \frac{\partial F}{\partial z}\frac{\partial z}{\partial u}. \qquad (5.19)$$

On the right, differentiation with respect to u is carried out with v constant, while differentiation with respect to one of the variables x, y or z is carried out with the other two held constant. But when x, y and z satisfy (5.18), F is identically zero and so the left-hand side of (5.19) is zero. Thus, the right-hand side, which has the form of a scalar product, vanishes, showing that the vector

$$\frac{\partial F}{\partial x}\mathbf{i} + \frac{\partial F}{\partial y}\mathbf{j} + \frac{\partial F}{\partial z}\mathbf{k} \qquad (5.20)$$

is orthogonal to the vector $\partial \mathbf{r}/\partial u$. Similarly, by differentiating F with respect to v, with u constant, we find that (5.20) is orthogonal to $\partial \mathbf{r}/\partial v$, and therefore must be in a direction normal to the surface $F = 0$. The vector function (5.20) is called the *gradient* of F, and is denoted by grad F. We have

$$\text{grad}(xyz - 1) = \mathbf{i}\frac{\partial}{\partial x}(xyz - 1) + \mathbf{j}\frac{\partial}{\partial y}(xyz - 1) + \mathbf{k}\frac{\partial}{\partial z}(xyz - 1)$$

$$= yz\mathbf{i} + xz\mathbf{j} + xy\mathbf{k}.$$

If $u = \frac{1}{2}, v = \frac{1}{3}$, then $x = \frac{1}{2}, y = \frac{1}{3}$, and $z = 6$, according to (5.18), and so

$$\text{grad}(xyz - 1) = 2\mathbf{i} + 3\mathbf{j} + \tfrac{1}{6}\mathbf{k}$$

$$= \tfrac{1}{6}(12\mathbf{i} + 18\mathbf{j} + \mathbf{k}).$$

This agrees with the normal direction as found previously. □

Whenever the equation of a surface is given in the *implicit* form $F(x, y, z) = 0$, the normal direction at any point is most easily found by calculation of the gradient vector.

Problem 5.12 Find the equation of the tangent plane to the surface $x = y^3 + z^3$ at the point $(7, 2, -1)$ on it.

Solution. Write $F = x - y^3 - z^3$. A normal vector to the surface $F = 0$ at the point (x, y, z) is

$$\mathbf{n} = \text{grad}\, F = \mathbf{i}\frac{\partial}{\partial x}(x - y^3 - z^3) + \mathbf{j}\frac{\partial}{\partial y}(x - y^3 - z^3) + \mathbf{k}\frac{\partial}{\partial z}(x - y^3 - z^3)$$

$$= \mathbf{i} - 3y^2\mathbf{j} - 3z^2\mathbf{k}.$$

At the point $(7, 2, -1)$, $\mathbf{n} = \mathbf{i} - 12\mathbf{j} - 3\mathbf{k}$, and therefore the tangent plane at this point has the equation

$$[\mathbf{r} - (7\mathbf{i} + 2\mathbf{j} - \mathbf{k})] \cdot (\mathbf{i} - 12\mathbf{j} - 3\mathbf{k}) = 0,$$

or

$$\mathbf{r} \cdot (\mathbf{i} - 12\mathbf{j} - 3\mathbf{k}) = -14.$$

The corresponding rectangular cartesian form is

$$x - 12y - 3z = -14.$$ □

When differential increments du, dv are made in u, v, respectively, the chain rule for differentials gives

$$d\mathbf{r} = \frac{\partial \mathbf{r}}{\partial u}du + \frac{\partial \mathbf{r}}{\partial v}dv, \tag{5.21}$$

where $\mathbf{r} = x(u, v)\mathbf{i} + y(u, v)\mathbf{j} + z(u, v)\mathbf{k}$. This vector lies in the tangent plane at the point under consideration, because it is a linear combination of vectors tangential to the parametric lines on the surface. The magnitude of the displacement (5.21) is ds, whose square is

$$ds^2 = d\mathbf{r} \cdot d\mathbf{r} = \left(\frac{\partial \mathbf{r}}{\partial u}\right)^2 du^2 + 2\frac{\partial \mathbf{r}}{\partial u} \cdot \frac{\partial \mathbf{r}}{\partial v}du\,dv + \left(\frac{\partial \mathbf{r}}{\partial v}\right)^2 dv^2. \tag{5.22}$$

This last expression is known variously as the *metric*, the *square of the line element*, or the *first fundamental form* for the surface. The geometry of a surface is characterized by its metric; the study of metrics being fundamental to the differential geometry of surfaces. ☐

Problem 5.13 Find the line element for the surface

$$x = u, \quad y = v, \quad z = 1/uv, \quad (u, v \text{ positive}).$$

Solution. In Problem 5.10, it was found this surface that

$$\frac{\partial \mathbf{r}}{\partial u} = \mathbf{i} - \frac{1}{u^2 v}\mathbf{k}, \quad \frac{\partial \mathbf{r}}{\partial v} = \mathbf{j} - \frac{1}{uv^2}\mathbf{k},$$

and so we have

$$\left(\frac{\partial \mathbf{r}}{\partial u}\right)^2 = 1 + \frac{1}{u^4 v^2}, \quad \frac{\partial \mathbf{r}}{\partial u} \cdot \frac{\partial \mathbf{r}}{\partial v} = \frac{1}{u^3 v^3}, \quad \left(\frac{\partial \mathbf{r}}{\partial v}\right)^2 = 1 + \frac{1}{u^2 v^4},$$

giving for the line element ds,

$$ds^2 = \left(1 + \frac{1}{u^4 v^2}\right)du^2 + \frac{2}{u^3 v^3}\, du\, dv + \left(1 + \frac{1}{u^2 v^4}\right)dv^2.$$

EXERCISES

1. Find (i) the unit tangent $\mathbf{t}$; (ii) the principal normal $\mathbf{n}$; (iii) the curvature κ; (iv) the binormal $\mathbf{b}$, at the point $(1, 2, 0)$ on the curve $x = 1 + u^2$, $y = 2\cos 2u$, $z = -2\sin 2u$.

2. Verify that the torsion is zero for any plane curve.

3. Calculate the curvature and torsion of the curve $x = a(u - \sin u)$, $y = a(1 - \cos u)$, $z = 4a \sin\frac{1}{2}u$, where a is a constant.

4. Determine the cartesian equations of the osculating plane and the rectifying plane at the point $(1, \frac{1}{2}\pi, \frac{1}{2}\pi)$ for the space curve $x = \sin u$, $y = u$, $z = u - \cos u$.

5. Show that the curve $x = a\sin^2 u$, $y = a\sin u\cos u$, $z = a\cos u$ lies on a sphere.

6. Find the tangent plane at the point $(u = \frac{1}{6}\pi, v = \frac{1}{4}\pi)$ to the ellipsoid: $x = 2\sin u\cos v$, $y = 3\sin u\sin v$, $z = \cos u$.

7. Calculate the metrics for the following surfaces: (i) the cylinder $x = a\cos\theta$, $y = a\sin\theta$, $z = z$ (taking θ and z as parameters); (ii) the

sphere $x = a \sin \theta \cos \phi$, $y = a \sin \theta \sin \phi$, $z = a \cos \theta$; (iii) the ellipsoid in Exercise 6. Give the implicit equations of these surfaces.

8. Find the tangent plane at the point $(5, 3, 1)$ to the surface $15(x^2 - y^2)z^2 = 16xy$.

9. Prove that if $\mathbf{r} = x(t)\mathbf{i} + y(t)\mathbf{j} + z(t)\mathbf{k}$ is a plane curve, then $\dot{\mathbf{r}} \cdot (\ddot{\mathbf{r}} \wedge \dddot{\mathbf{r}}) = 0$. [*Hint*: show that $\mathbf{r}' \cdot (\mathbf{r}'' \wedge \mathbf{r}''') = 0$, by (5.8), and use $\mathbf{r}' = \dot{\mathbf{r}} \, dt/ds$.]

Chapter 6

Motion of a Particle

6.1 Projectiles In this section the earth's rotation is neglected, and it is assumed that the only forces acting are due to gravity (taken to be uniform over the region of interest) and, where stated, air resistance.

Problem 6.1 Integrate the equation of motion for a projectile when air resistance is negligible.

Solution. Let the direction and magnitude of the acceleration due to gravity be denoted by the constant vector g. If the mass of the particle is m, then according to Newton's second law the equation of motion is

$$\frac{d}{dt}(m\dot{\mathbf{r}}) = m\mathbf{g}, \tag{6.1}$$

where $\mathbf{r}$ is the position vector of the particle relative to a fixed origin, and $\dot{\mathbf{r}} = d\mathbf{r}/dt$ is the velocity vector. Assuming m to be constant, we have

$$\ddot{\mathbf{r}} = \mathbf{g}. \tag{6.2}$$

This equation can be integrated successively to give

$$\dot{\mathbf{r}} = \mathbf{g}t + \mathbf{A},$$

$$\mathbf{r} = \tfrac{1}{2}\mathbf{g}t^2 + \mathbf{A}t + \mathbf{B},$$

where $\mathbf{A}$ and $\mathbf{B}$ are constant vectors which depend on the initial conditions of the motion. Suppose that the point of projection is taken as origin, and that the particle is projected with velocity $\mathbf{V}$, at time $t = 0$. Then, $\dot{\mathbf{r}} = \mathbf{V}$ when $t = 0$, giving $\mathbf{A} = \mathbf{V}$. Also, $\mathbf{r} = 0$ when $t = 0$, so that $\mathbf{B} = 0$. We thus have

$$\mathbf{r} = \tfrac{1}{2}\mathbf{g}t^2 + \mathbf{V}t \tag{6.3}$$

as the position vector of the particle at any time t after projection.

The path lies in a plane, determined by the vectors $\mathbf{V}$ and $\mathbf{g}$ drawn from the origin as initial point. If we introduce rectangular cartesian coordinates with Oz vertically upwards and the plane Oxz as the plane of the motion, then we may write

$$\mathbf{g} = -g\mathbf{k}, \quad \mathbf{V} = V(\cos\alpha\,\mathbf{i} + \sin\alpha\,\mathbf{k}),$$

where α is the angle of projection, i.e. the angle of inclination of V to the horizontal. Putting $\mathbf{r} = x\mathbf{i} + y\mathbf{j} + z\mathbf{k}$, we get from (6.3),

$$x = Vt\cos\alpha, \quad y = 0, \quad z = -\tfrac{1}{2}gt^2 + Vt\sin\alpha,$$

which gives the coordinates at time t. Elimination of t gives the path in the xz plane;

$$z = -\tfrac{1}{2}g\left(\frac{x}{V\cos\alpha}\right)^2 + x\tan\alpha$$

which is the equation of a parabola with vertex upwards, at the point $x = (V^2/g)\sin\alpha\cos\alpha$, $z = (V^2/2g)\sin^2\alpha$, and semi-latus rectum $(V^2/g)\cos^2\alpha$. □

Problem 6.2 Integrate the equation of motion of a projectile when there is air resistance proportional to the velocity.

Solution. In the notation of the last problem, we may write the force due to air resistance as $-Km\dot{\mathbf{r}}$, where K is a positive constant. The equation of motion reduces to

$$\ddot{\mathbf{r}} = \mathbf{g} - K\dot{\mathbf{r}}, \tag{6.4}$$

in place of (6.2). This can be integrated once to give

$$\dot{\mathbf{r}} = \mathbf{g}t - K\mathbf{r} + \mathbf{A},$$

where $\mathbf{A}$ is a constant vector. As before, let us suppose that $\mathbf{r} = 0$, $\dot{\mathbf{r}} = \mathbf{V}$ at $t = 0$. Then $\mathbf{A} = \mathbf{V}$, and

$$\dot{\mathbf{r}} = \mathbf{g}t - K\mathbf{r} + \mathbf{V}. \tag{6.5}$$

Because the unknown $\mathbf{r}$ appears on the right, we cannot immediately integrate again. However, if we substitute for $\dot{\mathbf{r}}$ from the last equation into (6.4) we obtain

$$\ddot{\mathbf{r}} - K^2\mathbf{r} = \mathbf{g} - K\mathbf{V} - K\mathbf{g}t, \tag{6.6}$$

which can be solved in two stages. Consider the 'reduced' equation

$$\ddot{\mathbf{r}} - K^2\mathbf{r} = 0. \tag{6.7}$$

By treating separately the corresponding scalar equations

$$\ddot{x} - K^2x = 0, \quad \ddot{y} - K^2y = 0, \quad \ddot{z} - K^2z = 0,$$

we find that a solution of (6.7) is

$$\mathbf{r} = \mathbf{B}e^{Kt} + \mathbf{C}e^{-Kt}, \tag{6.8}$$

where $\mathbf{B}$ and $\mathbf{C}$ are arbitrary constant vectors. This is the general solution of (6.7), since the general solutions of the three scalar differential equations each depend on two arbitrary constant scalars. By adding to the right-hand side of (6.8) any *particular integral* of (6.6), we obtain the general solution of the latter. (See any standard text on the elementary theory of linear differential equations; but we naturally expect the motion to be entirely determined by two vectors, such as the initial position and velocity vectors of the particle.)

A particular integral of (6.6) is, by inspection,

$$\mathbf{r} = -(\mathbf{g} - K\mathbf{V} - K\mathbf{g}t)/K^2,$$

66

and so the general solution of (6.6) is

$$\mathbf{r} = \mathbf{B}e^{Kt} + \mathbf{C}e^{-Kt} - [(1 - Kt)\mathbf{g} - K\mathbf{V}]/K^2. \tag{6.9}$$

On substituting $\mathbf{r} = 0$, $\dot{\mathbf{r}} = \mathbf{V}$ when $t = 0$, in the last equation and its derivative with respect to t, we get

$$0 = \mathbf{B} + \mathbf{C} - (1/K^2)(\mathbf{g} - K\mathbf{V})$$
$$\mathbf{V} = K(\mathbf{B} - \mathbf{C}) + \mathbf{g}/K,$$

whence
$$\mathbf{B} = 0, \quad \mathbf{C} = (1/K^2)(\mathbf{g} - K\mathbf{V}).$$

Therefore, the position vector of the particle at any time t after projection is given by

$$\mathbf{r} = (1/K^2)[(K\mathbf{V} - \mathbf{g})(1 - e^{-Kt}) + K\mathbf{g}t],$$

and the velocity vector by

$$\dot{\mathbf{r}} = (1/K^2)[(K\mathbf{V} - \mathbf{g})Ke^{-Kt} + K\mathbf{g}] = \mathbf{g}/K + (\mathbf{V} - \mathbf{g}K)e^{-Kt}.$$

The last equation shows that the velocity tends to a definite value $\mathbf{g}/K$ as t tends to infinity; this is known as the *terminal velocity*. □

The elimination of $\dot{\mathbf{r}}$ between (6.4) and (6.5) provides a useful method of integrating the equation of motion because the second derivative on the right-hand side of (6.6) vanishes, enabling us to find a particular integral by putting $\ddot{\mathbf{r}} = 0$. One might alternatively attempt to solve (6.5) by writing it in the form

$$\dot{\mathbf{r}} + K\mathbf{r} = \mathbf{g}t + \mathbf{V}. \tag{6.10}$$

The reduced equation corresponding to (6.10) is

$$\dot{\mathbf{r}} + K\mathbf{r} = 0,$$

which has the solution

$$\mathbf{r} = \mathbf{D}e^{-Kt},$$

where $\mathbf{D}$ is an arbitrary constant vector.

The general solution of (6.10) consists of the sum of any particular integral and the term $\mathbf{D}e^{-Kt}$. However, it is not as easy to spot a particular integral for (6.10) as it was for (6.6), and for this reason the former method is preferable.

6.2 Resolutes of Acceleration
Problem 6.3 A point P in the xy plane has cartesian coordinates (x, y) and *plane polar coordinates* (r, θ) (Fig. 6.1), where

$$x = r\cos\theta, \quad y = r\sin\theta, \quad (r \geqslant 0, \quad 0 \leqslant \theta < 2\pi).$$

If P describes a curve in the plane, so that r and θ are functions of the time t, determine the resolutes (i) of velocity, (ii) of acceleration, of P in the

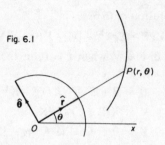

Fig. 6.1

directions of the perpendicular unit vectors $\hat{\mathbf{r}}$ and $\hat{\boldsymbol{\theta}}$, where $\mathbf{r} = \mathbf{OP}$ and $\hat{\boldsymbol{\theta}}$ points in the direction of θ increasing.

Solution. (i) We can write $\mathbf{r} = r\hat{\mathbf{r}}$, and so the velocity of P is

$$\mathbf{v} = \dot{\mathbf{r}} = \frac{d}{dt}(r\hat{\mathbf{r}}) = \dot{r}\hat{\mathbf{r}} + r\frac{d\hat{\mathbf{r}}}{dt}. \tag{6.11}$$

Now, by resolving,

$$\hat{\mathbf{r}} = \cos\theta\,\mathbf{i} + \sin\theta\,\mathbf{j}, \qquad \hat{\boldsymbol{\theta}} = -\sin\theta\,\mathbf{i} + \cos\theta\,\mathbf{j}, \tag{6.12}$$

and thus

$$d\hat{\mathbf{r}}/d\theta = -\sin\theta\,\mathbf{i} + \cos\theta\,\mathbf{j} = \hat{\boldsymbol{\theta}}, \tag{6.13}$$
$$d\hat{\boldsymbol{\theta}}/d\theta = -\cos\theta\,\mathbf{i} - \sin\theta\,\mathbf{j} = -\hat{\mathbf{r}},$$

whence

$$\frac{d\hat{\mathbf{r}}}{dt} = \frac{d\hat{\mathbf{r}}}{d\theta}\frac{d\theta}{dt} = \dot{\theta}\hat{\boldsymbol{\theta}}, \qquad \frac{d\hat{\boldsymbol{\theta}}}{dt} = \frac{d\hat{\boldsymbol{\theta}}}{d\theta}\frac{d\theta}{dt} = -\dot{\theta}\hat{\mathbf{r}}. \tag{6.14}$$

By the first of this pair of equations, we get from (6.11)

$$\mathbf{v} = \dot{r}\hat{\mathbf{r}} + r\dot{\theta}\hat{\boldsymbol{\theta}}, \tag{6.15}$$

so that the required resolutes of velocity are $\dot{r}$ and $r\dot{\theta}$ in the directions of $\hat{\mathbf{r}}$ and $\hat{\boldsymbol{\theta}}$, respectively.

(ii) Differentiating (6.15) with respect to t,

$$\begin{aligned}
\frac{d\mathbf{v}}{dt} &= \dot{r}\frac{d\hat{\mathbf{r}}}{dt} + \ddot{r}\hat{\mathbf{r}} + r\dot{\theta}\frac{d\hat{\boldsymbol{\theta}}}{dt} + (r\ddot{\theta} + \dot{r}\dot{\theta})\boldsymbol{\theta} \\
&= \dot{r}\dot{\theta}\hat{\boldsymbol{\theta}} + \ddot{r}\hat{\mathbf{r}} + r\dot{\theta}(-\dot{\theta}\hat{\mathbf{r}}) + (r\ddot{\theta} + \dot{r}\dot{\theta})\hat{\boldsymbol{\theta}} \\
&= (\ddot{r} - r\dot{\theta}^2)\hat{\mathbf{r}} + (r\ddot{\theta} + 2\dot{r}\dot{\theta})\hat{\boldsymbol{\theta}},
\end{aligned}$$

which shows that the resolutes of acceleration in the directions of $\hat{\mathbf{r}}$ and $\hat{\boldsymbol{\theta}}$ are $\ddot{r} - r\dot{\theta}^2$ and $r\ddot{\theta} + 2\dot{r}\dot{\theta}$, respectively. These are known as the *radial* and *transverse* resolutes of acceleration. $\square$

Problem 6.4 A particle P is constrained to move on the circle of radius a and centre O, in the xy plane, by a variable force whose direction at any instant bisects the angle between the direction of motion and the inward-drawn radius PO. If the speed is V at time $t = 0$, find the speed at any subsequent time.

68

Solution. In the notation of the last problem, we have $r = a$, so that $\dot{r} = \ddot{r} = 0$.

From the given direction of the variable force, it follows that the particle will move so that its resolutes of acceleration in the directions of $\hat{\theta}$ and $-\hat{r}$ are equal. Hence

$$r\ddot{\theta} = a\ddot{\theta} = -(-r\dot{\theta}^2) = a\dot{\theta}^2,$$

i.e.
$$\ddot{\theta} = \dot{\theta}^2.$$

This can be integrated by putting $u = \dot{\theta}^2$,

$$du/dt = 2\dot{\theta}\ddot{\theta} = 2\dot{\theta}^3 = 2u^{\frac{3}{2}},$$

$$u^{-\frac{3}{2}}\,du = 2\,dt,$$

$$u^{-\frac{1}{2}} = -t + C,$$

where C is a constant of integration. At $t = 0$, $u = \dot{\theta}^2 = V^2/a^2$, and so

$$a/V = C,$$

and we find that the speed at time t is

$$a\dot{\theta} = au^{\frac{1}{2}} = \frac{a}{a/V - t} = \frac{aV}{a - Vt}.$$

It is clear that this motion could not be sustained indefinitely, as the speed becomes infinite after a finite time $t = a/V$. For a material particle this would require an infinite amount of energy. $\qquad\Box$

Problem 6.5 A particle moves along the equiangular spiral $r = ae^{\theta \cot \alpha}$, where α and a are constants $(0 < \alpha < \frac{1}{2}\pi)$, at constant speed V in the sense of θ increasing. Show that the acceleration is normal to the direction of motion, and that the magnitude of the acceleration eventually tends to zero.

Solution. This example may be tackled using either the *tangential* and *normal* resolutes of acceleration (see p. 74), or the radial and transverse resolutes. Indeed, it follows by consideration of the former that whenever a particle describes a space curve with constant speed the direction of the acceleration is normal to the path. (This follows, too, from the fact that $d(\mathbf{v}.\mathbf{v})/dt = 0$.)

By differentiation with respect to time, we have

$$\dot{r} = ae^{\theta \cot \alpha}\dot{\theta} \cot \alpha = r\dot{\theta} \cot \alpha,$$

and so the ratio of the radial and transverse resolutes of velocity is a constant:

$$\dot{r}/r\dot{\theta} = \cot \alpha.$$

This shows that the direction of motion makes a constant angle α with OP, where P is the instantaneous position of the particle, and explains why the path is called an *equiangular spiral* (Fig. 6.2). By resolving the

69

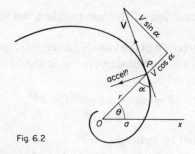

Fig. 6.2

velocity in the direction OP, we get

$$\dot{r} = V\cos\alpha,$$

and by the previous equation, or by resolving in the transverse direction,

$$r\dot{\theta} = V\sin\alpha.$$

If we take $\theta = 0, r = a$, as the position for which $t = 0$, then by integration we have

$$r = Vt\cos\alpha + a \qquad (6.16)$$

as the polar distance of the particle from the origin at any time t. Note that $\ddot{r} = 0$, and hence the radial and transverse resolutes of acceleration may be written

$$-r\dot{\theta}^2, \qquad r\ddot{\theta} + 2\dot{r}\dot{\theta} = \frac{1}{r}\frac{d}{dt}(r^2\dot{\theta}), \qquad (6.17)$$

respectively. But

$$\frac{d}{dt}(r^2\dot{\theta}) = \frac{d}{dt}[(Vt\cos\alpha + a)V\sin\alpha]$$

$$= V^2\sin\alpha\cos\alpha, \qquad (6.18)$$

by (6.16) and the preceding equation, and so the ratio of the resolutes of acceleration in the directions PO and $\hat{\theta}$ is, by (6.17),

$$r^2\dot{\theta}^2/V^2\sin\alpha\cos\alpha = V^2\sin^2\alpha/V^2\sin\alpha\cos\alpha$$

$$= \tan\alpha = \cot(\tfrac{1}{2}\pi - \alpha),$$

which confirms that the acceleration is in a direction making an angle $\tfrac{1}{2}\pi - \alpha$ with PO, and is thus along the inward normal to the spiral path.

By (6.16), r tends to infinity as t tends to infinity, and by comparing (6.17) and (6.18), we thus find that the transverse resolute of acceleration becomes vanishingly small after an infinite time, and so does the other resolute since the two are in a constant finite ratio. This gives the required result.

The result can also be interpreted in terms of the curvature of the path.

70

A calculation shows that the curvature tends to zero as P progresses infinitely far along the path. Since the speed is constant, the straighter the path, the less the acceleration. $\qquad\qquad\qquad\qquad\qquad\qquad\qquad\qquad\quad$ □

The *angular momentum* of a particle about a fixed point O is the moment, about O, of its linear momentum $m\mathbf{v}$, where m is the mass and $\mathbf{v}$ the velocity. Here, the linear momentum vector is to be considered localized at the particle, and therefore the angular momentum about O is $\mathbf{r}\wedge m\mathbf{v} = \mathbf{r}\wedge m\dot{\mathbf{r}}$, where $\mathbf{r}$ is the position vector of the particle relative to O. If the resultant force acting on the particle is $\mathbf{F}$, then by Newton's second law of motion,

$$\frac{d}{dt}(m\dot{\mathbf{r}}) = \mathbf{F},$$

and $\qquad\qquad \mathbf{r}\wedge\frac{d}{dt}(m\dot{\mathbf{r}}) = \frac{d}{dt}(\mathbf{r}\wedge m\dot{\mathbf{r}}) = \mathbf{r}\wedge\mathbf{F},$ $\qquad\quad$ (6.19)

which shows that the rate of change of angular momentum about a fixed point is equal to the moment of the resultant force about the point. In particular, when the force $\mathbf{F}$ is at all times parallel to $\mathbf{r}$, the angular momentum vector is a constant of the motion.

The *kinetic energy* of the particle is the scalar $T = \frac{1}{2}mv^2$. We have, when m is constant,

$$\frac{dT}{dt} = \frac{1}{2}\frac{d}{dt}(m\mathbf{v}\,.\,\mathbf{v}) = m\mathbf{v}\,.\,\frac{d\mathbf{v}}{dt} = \mathbf{F}\,.\,\mathbf{v},$$

and so the increase in kinetic energy between the times t_1 and t_2 is $\displaystyle\int_{t_1}^{t_2}\mathbf{F}\,.\,\mathbf{v}dt,$ which is the *work done* by the force $\mathbf{F}$ between these times. If the work done by $\mathbf{F}$ is zero, as, for example, when $\mathbf{F}$ is at all times perpendicular to $\mathbf{v}$, then T is a constant of the motion.

Problem 6.6 A particle moves under a *central force* directed towards the origin O. Show that the motion takes place in a fixed plane, and that the *areal velocity* is constant.

If the magnitude of the force is proportional to the inverse square of the distance of the particle from O, so that $\mathbf{F} = -(m\mu/r^2)\mathbf{r}$, where μ is a positive constant, show that the path is a conic with O as a focus. In particular, if the path is an ellipse, show that the speed v is given by

$$v^2 = \mu\left(\frac{2}{r} - \frac{1}{a}\right),$$

where a is the semi-major axis.

Solution. A *central force* is one which is always directed towards a particular fixed point called the *centre*, in this case the origin O. In most practical cases, the magnitude of the force is a function only of the distance r from the centre. (The inverse square law arises, for example, in the gravitational theory of planetary motion, and in electromagnetic theory.) Since the moment of the force about the centre is zero, we have by (6.19) that

$$\mathbf{r} \wedge \dot{\mathbf{r}} = \mathbf{h} = \text{const.},$$

$\mathbf{h}$ being the angular momentum of the particle per unit mass. This equation shows that the position vector $\mathbf{r}$ of the particle relative to O is always perpendicular to a fixed vector $\mathbf{h}$, and therefore the motion takes place in the plane through O with normal $\mathbf{h}$.

The *areal velocity* about the point O of a particle P moving with velocity $\mathbf{v}$ (whether or not, as in this case, in a fixed plane) is defined to be the vector $\frac{1}{2}\mathbf{r} \wedge \mathbf{v}$, where $\mathbf{r} = \mathbf{OP}$. It is normal to the instantaneous plane of motion (the plane of $\mathbf{r}$ and $\mathbf{v}$) and its magnitude is the rate at which the radius OP sweeps out area. For, if $\mathbf{r}$ and $\mathbf{r} + \Delta\mathbf{r}$ are the position vectors of P at successive times t, $t + \Delta t$, respectively, then the area swept out during the small interval Δt is that contained in the triangle with vertices at $O, \mathbf{r}, \mathbf{r} + \Delta\mathbf{r}$, approximately. By Problem 1.34, this is equal to $\frac{1}{2}|\mathbf{r} \wedge (\mathbf{r} + \Delta\mathbf{r})| = \frac{1}{2}|\mathbf{r} \wedge \Delta\mathbf{r}|$. Dividing by Δt and taking the limit as Δt tends to zero gives the stated result. In the case in question, the areal velocity is $\frac{1}{2}\mathbf{h}$.

To prove that the path under an inverse square law force is a conic, consider the constant scalar

$$h^2 = (\mathbf{r} \wedge \mathbf{v}) \cdot \mathbf{h} = \mathbf{r} \cdot (\mathbf{v} \wedge \mathbf{h}). \tag{6.20}$$

we have

$$\frac{d}{dt}(\mathbf{v} \wedge \mathbf{h}) = \frac{d\mathbf{v}}{dt} \wedge \mathbf{h} = -\frac{\mu}{r^2} \hat{\mathbf{r}} \wedge \mathbf{h}. \tag{6.21}$$

The vector product $\mathbf{r} \wedge \mathbf{h}$ is perpendicular to both of its constituent vectors, and is therefore parallel to the plane of the motion and perpendicular to $\mathbf{r}$. This means that it must be a multiple of $\hat{\boldsymbol{\theta}}$. In fact,

$$\mathbf{h} = \mathbf{r} \wedge \mathbf{v} = r\hat{\mathbf{r}} \wedge (\dot{r}\hat{\mathbf{r}} + r\dot{\theta}\hat{\boldsymbol{\theta}}) = r^2\dot{\theta}(\hat{\mathbf{r}} \wedge \hat{\boldsymbol{\theta}}),$$

whence $h = r^2\dot{\theta}$ (which is an important relation) and

$$\hat{\mathbf{r}} \wedge \mathbf{h} = r^2\dot{\theta}\hat{\mathbf{r}} \wedge (\hat{\mathbf{r}} \wedge \hat{\boldsymbol{\theta}}) = -r^2\dot{\theta}\hat{\boldsymbol{\theta}}.$$

Therefore, (6.21) becomes

$$\frac{d}{dt}(\mathbf{v} \wedge \mathbf{h}) = \mu\dot{\theta}\hat{\boldsymbol{\theta}} = \mu\frac{d\hat{\mathbf{r}}}{dt},$$

by (6.14). Integrating,

$$\mathbf{v} \wedge \mathbf{h} = \mu\hat{\mathbf{r}} + \mathbf{a},$$

where $\mathbf{a} = \text{const.}$, and so by (6.20),

$$h^2 = \mu r + \mathbf{r} \cdot \mathbf{a} = \mu r + ar\cos\theta,$$

where θ is the angle between $\mathbf{r}$ and $\mathbf{a}$. Hence

$$\frac{h^2}{\mu r} = 1 + \frac{a}{\mu}\cos\theta, \qquad (6.22)$$

which is in the standard polar form

$$l/r = 1 + e\cos\theta \qquad (6.23)$$

for a conic of eccentricity e and semi-latus rectum l ($=h^2/\mu$), with the origin as a focus. According as e is less than, equal to, or greater than 1, the orbit is an ellipse, parabola or hyperbola.

To find the speed in terms of r, we multiply the equation

$$\ddot{\mathbf{r}} = -\frac{\mu}{r^3}\mathbf{r}$$

scalarly by $\dot{\mathbf{r}}$, giving

$$\dot{\mathbf{r}}.\ddot{\mathbf{r}} = \frac{d}{dt}(\dot{\mathbf{r}}.\dot{\mathbf{r}}) = \frac{1}{2}\frac{d}{dt}(v^2) = -\frac{\mu}{r^3}(\mathbf{r}.\dot{\mathbf{r}}) = -\frac{\mu}{r^3}(r\dot{r}) = \mu\frac{d}{dt}\left(\frac{1}{r}\right),$$

and on integrating,

$$v^2 = \frac{2\mu}{r} + C, \qquad (6.24)$$

where C is a constant. In the case of an elliptic orbit, the point of nearest approach ($r = l/(1+e)$, according to (6.23)) occurs when P is at the end of the major axis nearest the origin, which is a focus. Since OP is then perpendicular to the velocity, $h = rv = lv/(1+e)$, and so

$$C = v^2 - \frac{2\mu}{r} = \frac{h^2(1+e)^2}{l^2} - \frac{2\mu(1+e)}{l}.$$

But $h^2 = \mu l$, and we thus find

$$C = -\frac{\mu}{l}(1-e^2).$$

By a standard property of the ellipse, $l = a(1-e^2)$, and so (6.24) takes the required form,

$$v^2 = \mu\left(\frac{2}{r} - \frac{1}{a}\right).$$

When both sides are multiplied by $\frac{1}{2}m$, this becomes the *energy equation*, the potential energy of the particle being $-m\mu/r$ (to within an additive constant) when at distance r from O. $\qquad\square$

If a particle moves with velocity $\mathbf{v}$ along a space curve for which the unit tangent vector is $\mathbf{t}$ and the principal normal vector is $\mathbf{n}$, then $\mathbf{v} = v\mathbf{t}$, and the acceleration is

73

$$\frac{d\mathbf{v}}{dt} = \frac{d}{dt}(v\mathbf{t}) = \frac{dv}{dt}\mathbf{t} + v\frac{d\mathbf{t}}{dt}.$$

(Here, the time variable t should not be confused with the magnitude of $\mathbf{t}$, which is unity.) But, if s denotes arc distance along the curve, then by (5.2),

$$\frac{d\mathbf{t}}{dt} = \frac{ds}{dt}\frac{d\mathbf{t}}{ds} = v\kappa\mathbf{n} = \frac{v}{\rho}\mathbf{n},$$

where ρ is the radius of curvature. Therefore

$$\frac{d\mathbf{v}}{dt} = \frac{dv}{dt}\mathbf{t} + \frac{v^2}{\rho}\mathbf{n},$$

showing that the acceleration at any instant lies in the osculating plane, and has resolutes dv/dt *tangential* to the path and v^2/ρ in the direction of the (principal) *normal*.

Problem 6.7 A particle P moves along a space curve such that its position at time t is given by $x = t \cos \omega t$, $y = t \sin \omega t$, $z = t$, where ω is a positive constant. Describe the motion, and find the tangential and normal resolutes of acceleration at time $t = 0$.

Solution. The path lies on the surface $x^2 + y^2 = z^2$, and since the left-hand side of this equation is the square of the distance from Oz, the surface is evidently one of revolution about this axis. It is, in fact, a 'vertical' cone of semi-vertical angle $\pi/4$, because each point on it is equidistant from the z axis and the plane $z = 0$. If P_0 denotes the projection of the point P on the plane $z = 0$, then the angle between OP_0 and Ox is

$$\theta = \tan^{-1}(y/x) = \omega t,$$

which shows that the angle θ increases uniformly with t. Furthermore, z also increases uniformly with t, and it follows that the motion is one in which P traces, on the cone, a contracting spiral (for $t < 0$) and an expanding spiral (for $t > 0$), while 'climbing' and turning at a constant rate. We have

$$\mathbf{v} = \dot{x}\mathbf{i} + \dot{y}\mathbf{j} + \dot{z}\mathbf{k}$$
$$= (\cos \omega t - \omega t \sin \omega t)\mathbf{i} + (\sin \omega t + \omega t \cos \omega t)\mathbf{j} + \mathbf{k}, \qquad (6.25)$$

whence $v^2 = 2 + \omega^2 t^2$, and

$$d\mathbf{v}/dt = \omega(-2\sin \omega t - \omega t \cos \omega t)\mathbf{i} + \omega(2\cos \omega t - \omega t \sin \omega t)\mathbf{j}. \quad (6.26)$$

The unit tangent vector to the path is

$$\mathbf{t} = \mathbf{v}/v = (2 + \omega^2 t^2)^{-\frac{1}{2}}\mathbf{v},$$

and so
$$\frac{d\mathbf{t}}{ds} = \frac{d\mathbf{t}}{dt} \bigg/ \frac{ds}{dt} = (2 + \omega^2 t^2)^{-\frac{1}{2}}\frac{d\mathbf{t}}{dt}$$

$$= \frac{1}{2+\omega^2 t^2} \frac{d\mathbf{v}}{dt} - \frac{\omega^2 t\mathbf{v}}{(2+\omega^2 t^2)^2}.$$

Hence, when $t = 0$, we have for the radius of curvature ρ,

$$\kappa = 1/\rho = |d\mathbf{t}/ds| = \tfrac{1}{2}|d\mathbf{v}/dt| = \tfrac{1}{2}|2\omega\mathbf{j}| = \omega, \qquad \text{by (6.26)},$$

giving for the normal resolute of acceleration at this time

$$v^2/\rho = 2\omega,$$

the tangential resolute being

$$\frac{dv}{dt} = \left[\frac{d}{dt}(2+\omega^2 t^2)^{\frac{1}{2}} \right]_{t=0} = 0. \qquad \square$$

6.3 Charged Particle in a Uniform Magnetic Field   An important example of a particle in motion is that of an electrically charged particle in an electromagnetic field. If $\mathbf{E}$ and $\mathbf{B}$ are the electric and magnetic field vectors respectively, then the force on a particle whose charge is e and velocity $\mathbf{v}$ is (in SI units)

$$\mathbf{F} = e(\mathbf{E} + \mathbf{v} \wedge \mathbf{B}).$$

Provided that the speed of the particle is not comparable with the speed of light, the mass m is constant, and the equation of motion is therefore

$$\ddot{\mathbf{r}} = \alpha(\mathbf{E} + \dot{\mathbf{r}} \wedge \mathbf{B}),$$

where α denotes e/m. In many physical situations the electric field $\mathbf{E}$ is zero and the magnetic field $\mathbf{B}$ is constant.

Problem 6.8   A charged particle is projected with velocity $\mathbf{V}$ in the presence of a uniform magnetic field $\mathbf{B}$, gravity being negligible. Prove that the speed of the particle is constant, and that if $\mathbf{V}$ is perpendicular to $\mathbf{B}$ the path is a circle of radius $V/\alpha B$.

Solution. The equation of motion is

$$\ddot{\mathbf{r}} = \alpha\dot{\mathbf{r}} \wedge \mathbf{B}. \qquad (6.27)$$

Scalar multiplication by $\dot{\mathbf{r}}$ gives $d(\dot{\mathbf{r}} \cdot \dot{\mathbf{r}})/dt = 0$, whence the speed is constant. (Note that this holds irrespectively of the fact that $\mathbf{B}$ is constant.) Integration of (6.27) leads to the equation

$$\dot{\mathbf{r}} = \alpha\mathbf{r} \wedge \mathbf{B} + \mathbf{V}, \qquad (6.28)$$

provided that the origin is taken at the point of projection. It follows that $\dot{\mathbf{r}} \cdot \mathbf{B} = \mathbf{V} \cdot \mathbf{B} = 0$ (given), and on integrating,

$$\mathbf{r} \cdot \mathbf{B} = \text{const.} = 0,$$

since $\mathbf{r} = 0$ initially. Therefore the motion is confined to the plane through the point of projection normal to $\mathbf{B}$.

Since $\mathbf{V}$ is perpendicular to $\mathbf{B}$, we can write $\mathbf{V} = \alpha\mathbf{C}\wedge\mathbf{B}$, for a certain vector $\mathbf{C}$ in the plane of motion. Then (6.28) becomes

$$\dot{\mathbf{r}} = \alpha(\mathbf{r}+\mathbf{C})\wedge\mathbf{B},$$

and if we move the origin to the point $\mathbf{r} = -\mathbf{C}$ by writing $\mathbf{R} = \mathbf{r}+\mathbf{C}$, we get a simplified form of (6.28),

$$\dot{\mathbf{R}} = \alpha\mathbf{R}\wedge\mathbf{B} = (-\alpha\mathbf{B})\wedge\mathbf{R}. \tag{6.29}$$

It follows that the particle moves as though it were attached to a rigid body which rotates with angular velocity $-\alpha\mathbf{B}$ about the point $\mathbf{R} = 0$, i.e. $\mathbf{r} = -\mathbf{C}$. When $\mathbf{r} = 0$, $\mathbf{R} = \mathbf{C}$, and since this point is on the path, the latter is a circle of radius C, where

$$V = |\alpha\mathbf{C}\wedge\mathbf{B}| = \alpha CB,$$

giving $C = V/\alpha B$ as required.

We note that as the speed has the constant value V, the period of rotation is $2\pi C/V = 2\pi/\alpha B$, which is independent of V. If the charge e is positive, the sense of rotation is negative with respect to $\mathbf{B}$ in view of the minus sign in (6.29). $\qquad\square$

Problem 6.9 Describe the motion of the particle in the last problem if all conditions are the same except that the initial velocity $\mathbf{V}$ is not perpendicular to $\mathbf{B}$.

Solution. We again have (6.28). By multiplying scalarly by $\mathbf{B}$, we find $\dot{\mathbf{r}}.\mathbf{B} = \mathbf{V}.\mathbf{B} = $ const., i.e. the resolute of velocity in the direction of $\mathbf{B}$ is constant. Let

$$\mathbf{V} = \mathbf{V}_1+\mathbf{V}_2,$$

where $\mathbf{V}_1$ is perpendicular to $\mathbf{B}$ and $\mathbf{V}_2$ is parallel to $\mathbf{B}$. Then

$$\dot{\mathbf{r}} = \alpha\mathbf{r}\wedge\mathbf{B}+\mathbf{V}_1+\mathbf{V}_2.$$

Writing $\mathbf{s} = \mathbf{r}-\mathbf{V}_2 t$, we obtain

$$\dot{\mathbf{s}} = \dot{\mathbf{r}}-\mathbf{V}_2 = \alpha\mathbf{r}\wedge\mathbf{B}+\mathbf{V}_1 = \alpha\mathbf{s}\wedge\mathbf{B}+\mathbf{V}_1, \tag{6.30}$$

since $\mathbf{V}_2\wedge\mathbf{B} = 0$. Therefore, $\mathbf{s}$ now plays the role played by $\mathbf{r}$ in the last problem, since (6.30) is identical in form with (6.28), with $\mathbf{V}_1$ (which is perpendicular to $\mathbf{B}$) in place of $\mathbf{V}$.

The significance of $\mathbf{s}$ is that it is the position vector of the particle relative to an origin moving with velocity $\mathbf{V}_2$. By the last problem, relative to the moving origin the motion is circular in a plane perpendicular to $\mathbf{B}$, and therefore relative to the stationary origin ($\mathbf{r} = 0$) the particle moves in a circular helix with axis parallel to $\mathbf{B}$. If e is positive, the helix is described in the sense of a left-handed screw; each complete turn takes the same time, $2\pi/\alpha B$, as one revolution in the former case of a circular path. $\qquad\square$

According to the special theory of relativity, when a particle moves with speed **v** in an inertial (uniformly moving, non-rotating) reference frame, its mass is $m = m_0(1 - v^2/c^2)^{-\frac{1}{2}}$, where m_0 is its mass when at rest. With this modification, the second law of motion remains valid; and the force on a moving charged particle in an electromagnetic field is again

$$\mathbf{F} = e(\mathbf{E} + \mathbf{v} \wedge \mathbf{B}).$$

Problem 6.10 Show that in the relativistic case the speed of a charged particle projected into a uniform magnetic field is again constant. Deduce that the nature of the ensuing motion is the same as in Problem 6.8 or 6.9.

Solution. The equation of motion is

$$d(m\mathbf{v})/dt = e\mathbf{v} \wedge \mathbf{B}, \tag{6.31}$$

where $m = m_0(1 - v^2/c^2)^{-\frac{1}{2}}$. Multiplying scalarly by $m\mathbf{v}$ gives

$$\tfrac{1}{2}\frac{d}{dt}(m\mathbf{v} \cdot m\mathbf{v}) = \tfrac{1}{2}m_0^2 \frac{d}{dt}\left(\frac{v^2}{1 - v^2/c^2}\right) = 0.$$

The quantity differentiated in the second term is therefore constant, and it follows that the speed v must be constant.

From the relation between mass and speed it is seen that the mass m is constant throughout the motion, and so the problem reduces to that of Problem 6.8 or 6.9 according as the velocity of projection is, or is not, perpendicular to **B**. The period of rotation in this case depends on the speed, since this enters into $\alpha = e/m$. ∎

6.4 Rotating Coordinate Systems Let $Oxyz$ and $Ox'y'z'$ be two sets of rectangular axes, denoted by S and S' respectively, sharing a common origin O but having different orientations in space. If primes are used for symbols in the second system, S', we have two component forms for a given vector **a**:

$$\mathbf{a} = a_1\mathbf{i} + a_2\mathbf{j} + a_3\mathbf{k} = a_1'\mathbf{i}' + a_2'\mathbf{j}' + a_3'\mathbf{k}'. \tag{6.32}$$

An important case is when S' rotates (like a rigid body) with a certain angular velocity **ω** relative to S, which is regarded as 'fixed'. For example, S' might be attached to the earth, with centre as O, while S is non-rotating relative to the stars. The rates of change of **a** measured in the respective systems are written

$$\frac{d\mathbf{a}}{dt} = \dot{a}_1\mathbf{i} + \dot{a}_2\mathbf{j} + \dot{a}_3\mathbf{k}, \quad \left(\frac{d\mathbf{a}}{dt}\right)' = \dot{a}_1'\mathbf{i}' + \dot{a}_2'\mathbf{j}' + \dot{a}_3'\mathbf{k}'. \tag{6.33}$$

Since the triad of vector $\mathbf{i}', \mathbf{j}', \mathbf{k}'$ drawn from O rotates in the first system as a rigid body whose angular velocity is **ω**, we have

$$d\mathbf{i}'/dt = \mathbf{\omega} \wedge \mathbf{i}', \quad d\mathbf{j}'/dt = \mathbf{\omega} \wedge \mathbf{j}', \quad d\mathbf{k}'/dt = \mathbf{\omega} \wedge \mathbf{k}'. \tag{6.34}$$

We can relate the two expressions (6.33) by differentiating the right-hand member of (6.32) in the S system. Thus,

$$\frac{d\mathbf{a}}{dt} = \frac{d}{dt}(a_1'\mathbf{i}' + a_2'\mathbf{j}' + a_3'\mathbf{k}'),$$

where

$$\frac{d}{dt}(a_1'\mathbf{i}') = \dot{a}_1'\mathbf{i}' + a_1'\boldsymbol{\omega}\wedge\mathbf{i}', \qquad (6.35)$$

with corresponding expressions for the derivatives of the other two terms, according to (6.34). On adding the three expressions of the form (6.35) we get

$$d\mathbf{a}/dt = (d\mathbf{a}/dt)' + \boldsymbol{\omega}\wedge\mathbf{a},$$

by the second of (6.33).

Problem 6.11 Find the relation between the accelerations of a moving point P relative to S and to S'.

Solution. According to the last equation, the operation d/dt carried out on a vector in S gives rise to the same vector as the operation $(d/dt)' + \boldsymbol{\omega}\wedge$ carried out in S'. Thus, if $\mathbf{r} = \mathbf{OP}$, the acceleration relative to S is

$$\frac{d^2\mathbf{r}}{dt^2} = \left[\left(\frac{d}{dt}\right)' + \boldsymbol{\omega}\wedge\right]\left[\left(\frac{d\mathbf{r}}{dt}\right)' + \boldsymbol{\omega}\wedge\mathbf{r}\right]$$

$$= \left(\frac{d^2\mathbf{r}}{dt^2}\right)' + 2\boldsymbol{\omega}\wedge\left(\frac{d\mathbf{r}}{dt}\right)' + \left(\frac{d\boldsymbol{\omega}}{dt}\right)'\wedge\mathbf{r} + \boldsymbol{\omega}\wedge(\boldsymbol{\omega}\wedge\mathbf{r}), \qquad (6.36)$$

where the first term on the right is the acceleration in S'. $\qquad\square$

Since

$$\frac{d\boldsymbol{\omega}}{dt} = \left(\frac{d\boldsymbol{\omega}}{dt}\right)' + \boldsymbol{\omega}\wedge\boldsymbol{\omega} = \left(\frac{d\boldsymbol{\omega}}{dt}\right)',$$

the rate of change of $\boldsymbol{\omega}$ is the same in either system.

When $\boldsymbol{\omega}$ is the earth's angular velocity due to its axial rotation, then $\omega = 2\pi/86400$ rad/s, 86 400 being the number of seconds in 1 day. In many applications regarding motion relative to the earth, the last term in (6.36) is negligibly small as it is of order ω^2. Furthermore, in these applications the slight variation in $\boldsymbol{\omega}$ may usually be neglected, so that approximately,

$$\frac{d^2\mathbf{r}}{dt^2} = \left(\frac{d^2\mathbf{r}}{dt^2}\right)' + 2\boldsymbol{\omega}\wedge\left(\frac{d\mathbf{r}}{dt}\right)'. \qquad (6.37)$$

The *Coriolis acceleration* $2\boldsymbol{\omega}\wedge\mathbf{v}'$, where $\mathbf{v}'$ denotes velocity in the rotating system, is present whenever $\mathbf{v}'$ is not parallel to $\boldsymbol{\omega}$, and it is perpendicular to both $\mathbf{v}'$ and $\boldsymbol{\omega}$.

Problem 6.12   A particle has position $\mathbf{r} = 2t\mathbf{i}' + t^2\mathbf{j}' + e^t\mathbf{k}'$ in $S'(Ox'y'z')$ at time t. It is observed that S' is rotating with variable angular velocity $\boldsymbol{\omega} = 3\mathbf{i}' + t\mathbf{j}' - e^{2t}\mathbf{k}'$ relative to a 'fixed' system $S(Oxyz)$. Find the true velocity and acceleration of the particle (i.e. relative to the fixed system) at time $t = 0$.

Solution. The velocity and acceleration in S' at time t are respectively

$$(d\mathbf{r}/dt)' = 2\mathbf{i}' + 2t\mathbf{j}' + e^t\mathbf{k}',$$
$$(d^2\mathbf{r}/dt^2)' = 2\mathbf{j}' + e^t\mathbf{k}'.$$

We find

$$(d\boldsymbol{\omega}/dt)' = \mathbf{j}' - 2e^{2t}\mathbf{k}' = \mathbf{j}' - 2\mathbf{k}', \qquad \boldsymbol{\omega} \wedge \mathbf{r} = -3\mathbf{j}',$$

at $t = 0$. Therefore, at this time the true velocity is

$$d\mathbf{r}/dt = (d\mathbf{r}/dt)' + \boldsymbol{\omega} \wedge \mathbf{r} = 2\mathbf{i}' + \mathbf{k}' + (-3\mathbf{j}')$$
$$= 2\mathbf{i}' - 3\mathbf{j}' + \mathbf{k}'.$$

By substituting these values into the right-hand side of (6.36), we find that the true acceleration is then

$$d^2\mathbf{r}/dt^2 = 2\mathbf{j}' + \mathbf{k}' + 2(3\mathbf{i}' - \mathbf{k}') \wedge (2\mathbf{i}' + \mathbf{k}') + (\mathbf{j}' - 2\mathbf{k}') \wedge \mathbf{k}' + (3\mathbf{i}' - \mathbf{k}') \wedge (-3\mathbf{j}')$$
$$= -2(\mathbf{i}' + 4\mathbf{j}' + 4\mathbf{k}'). \qquad \square$$

For the motion of a projectile or falling body, when the earth's rotation is to be taken into account, one may start with the equation

$$m\, d^2\mathbf{r}/dt^2 = \mathbf{F} = m\mathbf{g},$$

where $\mathbf{g}$ is the true acceleration due to gravity. The latter is not identical to the apparent acceleration as determined with, say, plumb line and pendulum in the laboratory, because of rotational effects. The plumb line, for example, does not point directly towards the centre of the earth. However, the difference between the true and apparent gravitational acceleration is usually negligible; it is of order ω^2.

We shall, in the following problems, work only in the rotating system of earth and so no confusion will arise if, to simplify notation, we omit primes. By (6.37), the approximate equation of motion is, therefore,

$$\ddot{\mathbf{r}} + 2\boldsymbol{\omega} \wedge \dot{\mathbf{r}} = \mathbf{g}. \tag{6.38}$$

Problem 6.13   A construction worker drops a small object from a point at height h above the ground. It falls to the ground without obstruction and its motion is not appreciably affected by air resistance. If P is the point on the ground vertically below the point of release, find the deviation of the point of impact from P.

Solution. Let O be the centre of the earth, and let Oz be the vertical through P. If R is the radius of the earth, then the position vector of the point of release Q is $\mathbf{r} = (R+h)\mathbf{k}$ relative to O (Fig. 6.3). Let $\mathbf{s} = \mathbf{r} - (R+h)\mathbf{k}$. Substituting for $\mathbf{r}$ in (6.38) gives

$$\ddot{\mathbf{s}} + 2\boldsymbol{\omega} \wedge \dot{\mathbf{s}} = \mathbf{g}. \tag{6.39}$$

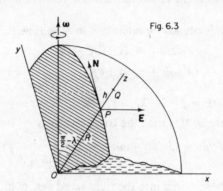

Fig. 6.3

It is convenient to work with $\mathbf{s}$ (the position vector of the object relative to Q) since at the moment of release ($t = 0$) we have simply $\mathbf{s} = \dot{\mathbf{s}} = 0$. Integrating (6.39),

$$\dot{\mathbf{s}} + 2\boldsymbol{\omega} \wedge \mathbf{s} = \mathbf{g}t,$$

and substituting back for $\dot{\mathbf{s}}$,

$$\ddot{\mathbf{s}} + 2\boldsymbol{\omega} \wedge (\mathbf{g}t - 2\boldsymbol{\omega} \wedge \mathbf{s}) = \ddot{\mathbf{s}} + 2\boldsymbol{\omega} \wedge \mathbf{g}t = \mathbf{g},$$

neglecting the term of order ω^2. We can integrate the last equation twice, using the initial conditions on $\mathbf{s}$, to get

$$\mathbf{s} = \tfrac{1}{2}\mathbf{g}t^2 - \tfrac{1}{3}\boldsymbol{\omega} \wedge \mathbf{g}t^3. \tag{6.40}$$

Let Ox be chosen parallel to the eastward horizontal at P, so that Oy is parallel to the northward horizontal. If λ is the (northerly) latitude of P, we see from the Figure that (resolving)

$$\boldsymbol{\omega} = \omega(\cos\lambda\mathbf{j} + \sin\lambda\mathbf{k}),$$

$$\mathbf{g} = -g\mathbf{k},$$

and so

$$\boldsymbol{\omega} \wedge \mathbf{g} = -\omega g \cos\lambda\mathbf{i}.$$

If we put $\mathbf{r} = x\mathbf{i} + y\mathbf{j} = z\mathbf{k}$ we get, by equating corresponding components in (6.40),

$$x = \tfrac{1}{3}\omega gt^3\cos\lambda, \quad y = 0, \quad z = R + h - \tfrac{1}{2}gt^2.$$

The object meets the horizontal plane through P when $z = R$, i.e. $t = 0$ (time of projection) or $t = (2h/g)^{\frac{1}{2}}$, which is the approximate time of fall, and also the well-known formula for the time of fall of a body when the earth's rotation is entirely neglected. At this time we have $y = 0$, and

80

$$x = \tfrac{2}{3}(2h/g)^{\frac{1}{2}}\,\omega h \cos\lambda,$$

which is the magnitude of the deviation of the point of impact from P; it is due eastwards. To give an idea of the extent of the deviation in a particular case: if $\lambda = 45°$ and $h = 200$ m, then the deviation is approximately 0·04 m. $\square$

Problem 6.14 A shot is fired with speed V due eastwards, at an angle of elevation α, from a point on the earth's surface at latitude λ north. If air resistance is negligible, show that when the shot strikes the ground it will have been deflected southwards an approximate distance

$$(4V^3\omega/g)\sin^2\alpha\cos\alpha\sin\lambda.$$

Solution. Take coordinate axes as in Problem 6.13, with P (Fig. 6.3) as point of firing. Let $\mathbf{s} = \mathbf{r} - R\mathbf{k}$, where R is the radius of the earth. The equation of motion is (6.39),

$$\ddot{\mathbf{s}} + 2\boldsymbol{\omega}\wedge\dot{\mathbf{s}} = \mathbf{g},$$

and the initial conditions are $\mathbf{s} = 0$, $\dot{\mathbf{s}} = \dot{\mathbf{r}} = \mathbf{V}$, where $\mathbf{V}$ is the velocity of projection. If $t = 0$ is taken as the moment of firing, then by integration we have

$$\dot{\mathbf{s}} + 2\boldsymbol{\omega}\wedge\mathbf{s} = \mathbf{g}t + \mathbf{V}.$$

Substituting back for $\dot{\mathbf{s}}$,

$$\ddot{\mathbf{s}} + 2\boldsymbol{\omega}\wedge(\mathbf{g}t + \mathbf{V}) = \mathbf{g},$$

neglecting a term of order ω^2. This equation can be integrated twice, using the initial conditions on $\mathbf{s}$ and $\dot{\mathbf{s}}$, to give

$$\mathbf{s} + \tfrac{1}{3}\boldsymbol{\omega}\wedge\mathbf{g}t^3 + \boldsymbol{\omega}\wedge\mathbf{V}t^2 = \tfrac{1}{2}\mathbf{g}t^2 + \mathbf{V}t. \qquad (6.41)$$

On putting

$$\mathbf{s} = \mathbf{r} - R\mathbf{k} = x\mathbf{i} + y\mathbf{j} + (z - R)\mathbf{k},$$
$$\boldsymbol{\omega} = \omega(\cos\lambda\,\mathbf{j} + \sin\lambda\,\mathbf{k}),$$
$$\mathbf{g} = -g\mathbf{k},$$
$$\mathbf{V} = V(\cos\alpha\,\mathbf{i} + \sin\alpha\,\mathbf{k})$$

in (6.41) and taking components we find

$$x = \tfrac{1}{3}\omega g t^3 \cos\lambda - \omega V t^2 \sin\alpha\cos\lambda + V t\cos\alpha, \qquad (6.42)$$
$$y = -\omega V t^2 \cos\alpha\sin\lambda, \qquad (6.43)$$
$$z = R + \omega V t^2 \cos\alpha\cos\lambda - \tfrac{1}{2}g t^2 + V t\sin\alpha. \qquad (6.44)$$

The time of flight is given, approximately, by putting $z = R$ in (6.44). Discarding the root $t = 0$, which corresponds to the instant of projection, we get

81

$$t = \frac{2V \sin \alpha}{g[1 - (2\omega V/g) \cos \alpha \cos \lambda]}$$

$$= \frac{2V \sin \alpha}{g} \left(1 + \frac{2\omega V}{g} \cos \alpha \cos \lambda \right),$$

by the binomial expansion, when terms of order ω^2 are neglected. At this time, to the same degree of approximation, the southward deviation is, by (6.43),

$$-y = \omega V (2V \sin \alpha/g)^2 \cos \alpha \sin \lambda$$

$$= (4V^3 \omega/g) \sin^2 \alpha \cos \alpha \sin \lambda,$$

as required.

EXERCISES

1. Find the maximum height attained by the projectile in Problem 6.1, and determine its range.

2. The position vector of a particle at time t is

$$\mathbf{r} = 2 \sin 2t \mathbf{i} - \cos 2t \mathbf{j} + 2(t + 1)\mathbf{k}.$$

Find the resolutes of its acceleration, tangential and normal to its path, at $t = 0$.

3. A particle describes the curve $x = u - \sin u$, $y = 1 - \cos u$, $z = 4 \sin \frac{1}{2}u$, at unit speed. Show that its acceleration, when at the point u, is $\frac{1}{4}(1 + \sin^2 \frac{1}{2}u)^{\frac{1}{2}}$ in the principal normal direction.

4. A particle of unit mass moves under a central force $-f(r)\hat{\mathbf{r}}$, $\mathbf{r}$ being its position vector relative to the centre and f a given function. Show that the radial and transverse equations of the (plane) motion are $\ddot{r} - r\dot{\theta}^2 = -f(r)$, $r^2\dot{\theta} = h$, where the angular momentum h is constant. Prove that if $u = 1/r$, then the path satisfies the differential equation

$$\frac{d^2u}{d\theta^2} + u = \frac{1}{h^2u^2} f\left(\frac{1}{u}\right).$$

[Hint: show that $\dot{r} = -(1/u^2)\dot{\theta}\, du/d\theta = -h\, du/d\theta$.]

5. Suppose that the reference system in Exercise 2 (there assumed 'fixed') were discovered to be, in fact, rotating with angular velocity $2t\mathbf{k}$. What would the true acceleration of the particle be at time t?

6. The equation of motion of a charged particle in an electromagnetic field is (c.f. § 6.3) $\ddot{\mathbf{r}} = \alpha(\mathbf{E} + \dot{\mathbf{r}} \wedge \mathbf{B})$. Transform this into the form applicable

in a coordinate system which is rotating with angular velocity ω. Show that if $\mathbf{B}$ is constant and B^2 is negligible, then the equation of motion can be reduced to

$$(d^2\mathbf{r}/dt^2)' = \alpha\mathbf{E},$$

by taking $\omega = -\frac{1}{2}\alpha\mathbf{B}$. (This result has application in the theory of the *Larmor precession*.)

7. A particle is projected vertically upwards with speed V from a point with northerly latitude λ. Show that it returns to earth with a deviation $4\omega V^3 \cos\lambda./3g^2$ to the west, where ω is the angular speed of the earth's rotation.

8. If a shot is fired eastwards with speed V from a point at northerly latitude λ, show that the increment in range due to the earth's rotation is approximately

$$(4\omega V^3/3g^2)(3 - 4\sin^2\alpha)\sin\alpha\cos\lambda,$$

where ω is the angular speed of the earth's rotation and α is the angle of elevation.

Answers to Exercises

Chapter 1

1. $3\mathbf{i}+2\mathbf{j}+6\mathbf{k}$, $-3\mathbf{i}-7\mathbf{j}-15\mathbf{k}$, $7\mathbf{j}+3\mathbf{k}$; $(-3, -6, -14)$.

2. $-\sqrt{2}(\mathbf{i}+\mathbf{j})$, $150(5+\sqrt{2}-\sqrt{6})^{\frac{1}{2}} \simeq 299$ km in the direction $15°59'$ south of west.

3. $\frac{1}{2}(\mathbf{b}+\mathbf{c})$, $\frac{1}{3}(\mathbf{a}+\mathbf{b}+\mathbf{c})$. The result follows by symmetry of the latter expression, and proves that the medians are concurrent in a point of trisection.

4. $a = \sqrt{6}$, $|2\mathbf{b}-\mathbf{c}| = 3\sqrt{6}$, $|\mathbf{a}+2\mathbf{b}-\mathbf{c}| = \sqrt{74}$.

5. Only the set $\mathbf{a}, \mathbf{b}, \mathbf{d}$.

6. $\cos^{-1}(4/\sqrt{30})$.

7. $\mathbf{r} = \mathbf{i}+\mathbf{k}+t(\mathbf{i}-\mathbf{j}+2\mathbf{k})$, $\mathbf{r}.(\mathbf{i}+\mathbf{j}) = 1$.
   Cartesian forms are $(x-1)/1 = y/-1 = (z-1)/2$, $x+y = 1$.

8. $\mathbf{r} = \mathbf{i}+t(\mathbf{i}+\mathbf{j}-3\mathbf{k})$.

9. $\sqrt{2}(-\mathbf{i}+\mathbf{j}+\sqrt{2}\mathbf{k})$, $(3-2\sqrt{2})\mathbf{i}+(1-2\sqrt{2})\mathbf{j}+\sqrt{2}\mathbf{k}$, $-(\mathbf{i}+\mathbf{j})$.

10. Angular speed 3 about an axis in the direction of $\mathbf{i}+2\mathbf{j}+2\mathbf{k}$.

Chapter 2

2. $\frac{1}{2}(\mathbf{i}+\mathbf{j}-\mathbf{k})$, $\frac{1}{2}(-\mathbf{i}+\mathbf{j}+\mathbf{k})$, $\frac{1}{2}(\mathbf{i}-\mathbf{j}+\mathbf{k})$.

3. $\mathbf{r}.(6\mathbf{i}-14\mathbf{j}+5\mathbf{k}) = 71$.

4. $-3\sqrt{2}(\mathbf{i}+\mathbf{j}+\mathbf{k})$, $5\sqrt{2}$.

5. $\mathbf{r} = \alpha\mathbf{a}' + \beta\mathbf{b}' + \gamma\mathbf{c}'$, where $\mathbf{a}', \mathbf{b}', \mathbf{c}'$ is the set reciprocal to $\mathbf{a}, \mathbf{b}, \mathbf{c}$.

7. $\mathbf{x} = [(\mathbf{a}\wedge \mathbf{b})/a^2]+\lambda\mathbf{a}$, $\mathbf{y} = -[(\mathbf{a}\wedge \mathbf{b})/a^2]+(1-\lambda)\mathbf{a}$, where λ is arbitrary, provided that $\mathbf{a} \neq 0$. When $\mathbf{a} = 0$, there is no solution unless $\mathbf{b} = 0$, in which case $\mathbf{x}$ is arbitrary and $\mathbf{y} = -\mathbf{x}$.

8. $\mathbf{x} = [(\mathbf{a}.\mathbf{b})\mathbf{a}+6\mathbf{b}+2\mathbf{a}\wedge \mathbf{c}]/2(6+a^2)$,
   $\mathbf{y} = [(\mathbf{a}.\mathbf{c})\mathbf{a}+6\mathbf{c}+3\mathbf{a}\wedge \mathbf{b}]/3(6+a^2)$.

Chapter 3

1. $3(\mathbf{j}+\mathbf{k})/\sqrt{2}$, $\sqrt{2}(-8\mathbf{i}+\mathbf{j}-\mathbf{k})$, $\mathbf{r} = \frac{2}{3}(-\mathbf{i}+8\mathbf{k})+t(\mathbf{j}+\mathbf{k})$.

2. (i) $p = \frac{1}{2}$, $q = -\frac{3}{2}$; (ii) p arbitrary, $q \neq -\frac{3}{2}$; (iii) $p \neq \frac{1}{2}$, $q = -\frac{3}{2}$.

3. (i) $67/3$, $-13/3$; (ii) $\mathbf{r} = (2/201)(7\mathbf{i}+5\mathbf{j}+20\mathbf{k})+\lambda(10\mathbf{i}-10\mathbf{j}-\mathbf{k})$; (iii) $-13/67$.

5. $\mathbf{j}+3\mathbf{k}$.

Chapter 4

1. $t(3t-2)\cos t - (t^3+2)\sin t + 2t$, $-(2+t^2\cos t + 2t\sin t)\mathbf{i}$
   $+ t(2\cos t - 3t - t\sin t)\mathbf{j} + [(3t-2)t\sin t + (t^3+2)\cos t]\mathbf{k}$.

3. (i) $\omega^2 t(\cos \omega t\,\mathbf{i} + \sin \omega t\,\mathbf{j})$, $\omega^2(\cos \omega t - \omega t\sin \omega t)\mathbf{i} +$
   $\omega^2(\sin \omega t + \omega t\cos \omega t)\mathbf{j}$; (ii) $\omega^2(1-\omega^2)/\sqrt{(1+\omega^2)}$.

4. $\mathbf{j}, \mathbf{i}, \pi(-\mathbf{i}+2\mathbf{k})$.

5. $-\mathbf{i}, \frac{1}{2}\pi(2\mathbf{i}-\mathbf{j})$.

7. $2\mathbf{i} - \frac{1}{2}(e^{\frac{1}{2}\pi}+1)\mathbf{j} + [(\pi-2)e^{\frac{1}{2}\pi}+2]\mathbf{k}$.

8. (i) $\hat{\mathbf{r}}+\mathbf{c}$; (ii) $(\mathbf{r}\wedge\dot{\mathbf{r}}).\ddot{\mathbf{r}}+c$; (iii) $(\mathbf{a}.\mathbf{r})\mathbf{r}\wedge\dot{\mathbf{r}}+\mathbf{c}$, where $\mathbf{c}$ denotes an arbitrary constant vector, and c an arbitrary constant scalar.

10. $\mathbf{r} = \frac{1}{2}(\sinh 2t - 2t)\mathbf{a}$.

Chapter 5

1. (i) $-\mathbf{k}$; (ii) $(\mathbf{i}-4\mathbf{j})/\sqrt{17}$; (iii) $(\sqrt{17})/8$, $-(4\mathbf{i}+\mathbf{j})/\sqrt{17}$.

3. $[\frac{1}{2}(3-\cos u)]^{\frac{1}{2}}/4a$, $-\cos \frac{1}{2}u\,(5-\cos u)/4a(3-\cos u)$.

4. $4y-2z = \pi, x = 1$.

6. $\mathbf{r}.(3\mathbf{i}+2\mathbf{j}+6\sqrt{6}\mathbf{k}) = 12\sqrt{2}$.

7. (i) $ds^2 = a^2\,d\theta^2 + dz^2$; (ii) $ds^2 = a^2(d\theta^2 + \sin^2\theta\,d\phi^2)$;
   (iii) $ds^2 = [1+\cos^2 u(3+5\sin^2 v)]du^2 + 10\sin u\cos u\sin v\cos v\,du\,dv +$
   $\sin^2 u(4+5\cos^2 v)dv^2$.
   $x^2+y^2 = a^2$, $x^2+y^2+z^2 = a^2$, $(x^2/4)+(y^2/9)+z^2 = 1$.

8. $51x-85y+240z = 240$.

Chapter 6

1. $(V^2/2g)\sin^2\alpha$, $(V^2/g)\sin 2\alpha$.

2. Tangential resolute zero, normal resolute 4.

5. $2[\cos 2t - 4(1+t+t^2)\sin 2t]\mathbf{i} + 4[\sin 2t + (1+4t+t^2)\cos 2t]\mathbf{j}$.

Index